Weight Training
Everyone

FIFTH EDITION

Joseph F. Signorile
David Sandler

Hunter Textbooks Inc.

ISBN: 0-88725-329-6

Hunter Textbooks Inc.

701 Shallowford Street,
Winston Salem, NC 27101

Additional copies of this textbook or other books on physical education subjects may be ordered through our World Wide Web site:
www.huntertextbooks.com
Printed in Canada

PREFACE

In the past 60 years, weight-training has diversified from a rehabilitation technique, to a training tool that addresses fitness, athletic performance, injury prevention and improvements in activities of daily living. The different reasons people weight train is reflected by the diversity among the people who engage in this activity. For this reason *Weight Training Everyone* is more than a collection of exercises. It is a comprehensive text that explains both the "hows" and "whys" of weight-training so that you have the tools to design a training program that can target your specific goals and maximize your results.

CONTENTS

CHAPTERS

CONTENTS

Chapter

1

Weight Training: The Concept and History

When the term "weight training" is used it often conjures up a picture of bodybuilders or competitive lifters pushing massive pieces of steel in an attempt to continually increase the size and strength of their skeletal muscles.

Figure 1-1

While this picture is still applicable for a portion of the population who weight-train, it is only a small part of the new concept of weight training that has evolved thanks to advances in training techniques, exercise science, and technology. Now weight training is seen as an integral part of any program designed for performance enhancement or wellness. In fact, it would be difficult to find an athletic or wellness training facility anywhere in the nation that does not incorporate weight training. Exercise scientists, strength coaches, personal trainers, and therapists are now actively developing weight training programs for populations from Olympic lifters to the frail elderly. This

Weight training programs are now being developed for populations from Olympic lifters to the frail elderly

Figure 1-2

new view of weight training as a tool to be used as part of an overall program tailored to the goals and needs of diverse populations is the basis of this text. By the end of the text we hope to have dispelled any illusion that a "one-size fits all" training program can fulfill the needs and aspirations of the millions of people who are currently flocking to the gyms and fitness centers throughout the world. We also hope to eliminate some of the mystery and confusion which are preventing millions of others from engaging in one of the most effective training methods available for increasing strength and power and changing body composition.

Let's begin with a look at the term "weight training". In effect, weight training is a catchall term used to describe the application of some type of resistance to a muscle in order to achieve a specific purpose or goal. Historically, (at least after the industrial revolution) this resistance was applied by lifting either barbells or dumbbells. Most of us have seen the old 110lb weight-lifting set with a flat bench that was the mainstay of most garages and backyard gyms (See figure 1-3). Technology has now expanded that picture. As you will see in Chapter 5 of this text, resistance can be provided using compressed air, hydraulics, electromagnets, rubber bands, composite rods, and any number of other devises that can apply a force that resists the muscle's movement. In addition, the use of various pulley and lever systems allows that resistance to be varied throughout the range of motion of the movement and can even control the speed at which a

110 lb. weight lifting set with a flat bench

Figure 1-3

movement is made. The importance of these new developments will be clarified when we review weight training equipment in Chapter 5.

The second part of the traditional picture, the use of weight training strictly for the development of muscle mass, has also been reshaped by exercise science and modern training methodology. While weight training can, without a doubt, increase the mass and strength of a skeletal muscle, this should not be considered its only use. In fact, the goals of specific lifting programs are as diverse as the needs and aspirations of the people who use them.

We can say with confidence that modern science has evolved weight training from a one-dimensional activity targeting strength and size to a multifaceted tool that can boost athletic performance, increase fitness, and enhance well-being as part of a healthy life style. In our chapter on program design (Chapter 10) we will show how specific programs can be tailored to increase athletic performance in various sports, decrease levels of body fat, and even "push back" the aging curve. Using the basic scientific principles explained in Chapters 2 and 3, we will provide examples of specific training programs and explain the principles that determine their success.

Finally, concepts that truly define the evolution of weight training as a fitness tool will be presented in Chapters 8, 9 and 10, but will be evident throughout the text. The concepts are the use of a diagnosis/prescription model and periodization cycling. These tools are designed to maximize the benefits of any weight training program.

This text is designed to be more than a simple catalogue of muscle groups and the lifting techniques that target them. It is a marriage of the "how's" and "why's" of weight training that readers can use to design and modify training programs as needs and goals evolve with changes in lifestyle, age, and fitness level. It is the use of this evolving diagnosis/prescription program that changes as the lifter changes that allows us to truly call this text "Weight Training Everyone".

Chapter

2

The Physiology of Weight Training

Weight training affects nearly every tissue of the body including nerves, muscles, connective tissues, and bones. Yet, the effects on muscle tissue have received the greatest attention by both the general public and fitness community. This may be due to the obvious active role of skeletal muscle and its rapid response to training, or it may be due to the fact that many lifts are named after the specific muscles targeted due to the strong influence that bodybuilding has had on resistance training techniques. This chapter will examine the structure and function of nerves, muscles, connective tissues, and bones and how weight training affects both their structure and function.

Nervous Tissue

The nerves of the human body dictate how our muscles contract. Movement patterns are sent to our muscles from the *motor cortex*, a very special area on the outer layer of our brain (see Figure 2-1).

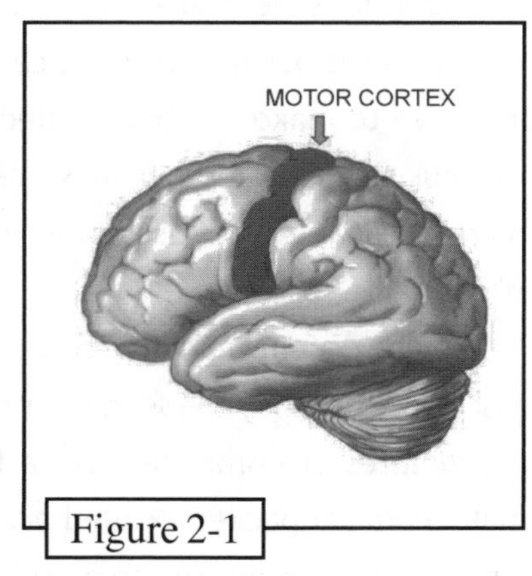

Figure 2-1

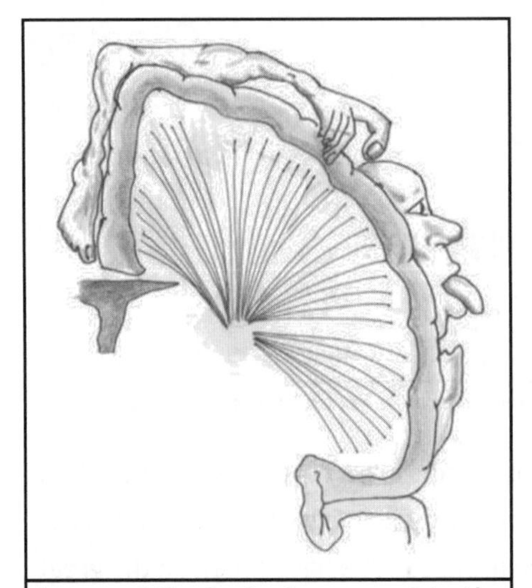

A map of the body drawn next to the motor cortex.

Figure 2-2

The motor cortex is arranged in sort of a "map" with specific body parts represented by different areas. When the map of the body is drawn next to the motor cortex, the parts that perform the most complex movements and get the greatest use make up the largest area. This forms a picture of a distorted man or *homunculus* (see Figure 2-2). Weight training can "rewire" the brain so that the areas we train actually get a larger area of the motor cortex and also receive more blood flow. This means that when you train a specific movement pattern you can actually "train your brain". Most fitness professionals who concentrate on lifting to improve performance recognize this and so the concept of movement pattern training rather than muscle training has become important.

In addition to your brain, you can also train the nerves (called *motor nerves*) that control your skeletal muscles. You can make the electrical message or *action potential* move more quickly along the nerve. This is because training can actually change the structure of the nerve to make it a better electrical conductor. This can effect both our strength and our movement speed since we can "call up" (*recruit*) and fire our muscles more powerfully (both quickly and with considerable force).

Weight training can also change the nerve endings that go to the muscles so that they can send their messages faster. The nerve endings or *endplates* are branched like a tree. All along the branches are small chemical packets (called *acetylcholine vesicles*) that are used to send the messages to the muscles that tell them to contract. The

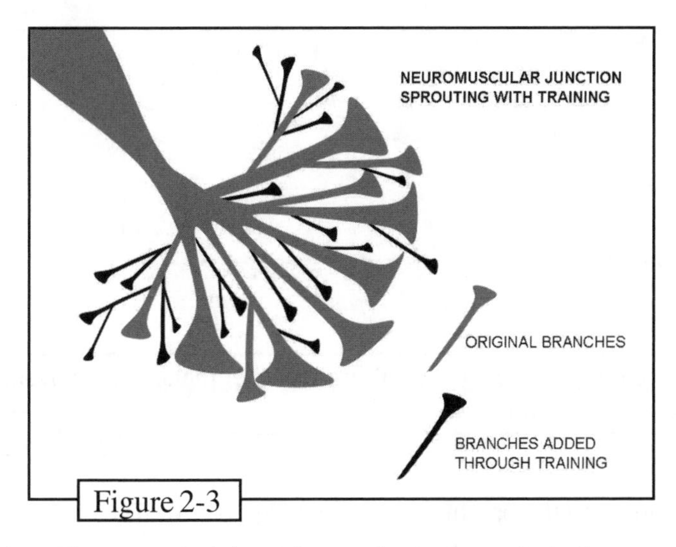

Figure 2-3

more branches your endplates have, the more packets they can send in a shorter amount of time, and the faster and harder your muscle can contract. It is like putting more people on the recipient list for your e-mail – more information goes out to more people in a shorter period of time. Weight training can actually increase the number of branches on your *motor endplates* (see Figure 2-3).

Finally, resistance training can increase the *synchronization* of the motor nerves going to *synergist* muscles. As you know, any movement you perform requires the use of more than one muscle. Let's take a simple movement like bending your arm (elbow flexion) as an example. The muscles involved in this movement are the two heads of the biceps brachii (*biceps* means *two heads* in Latin), the

Figure 2-4

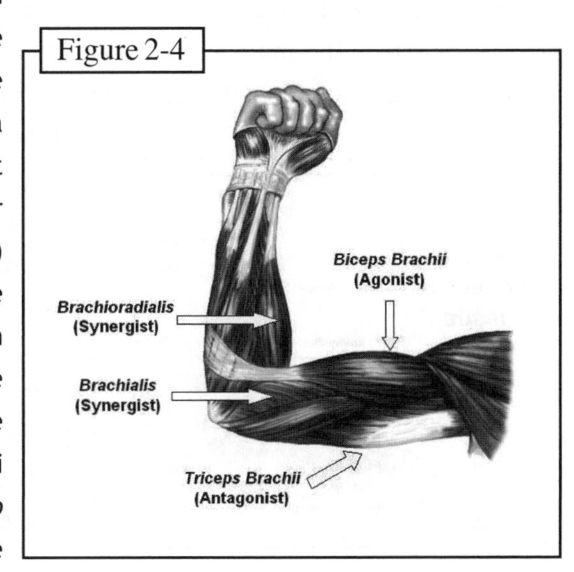

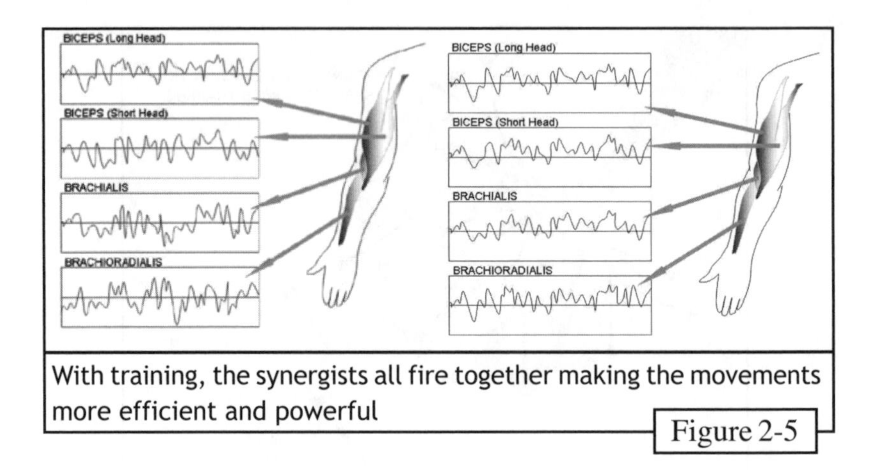

With training, the synergists all fire together making the movements more efficient and powerful

Figure 2-5

brachialis, and the brachioradialis (see Figure 2-4). The biceps brachii is the main muscle involved in elbow flexion and is therefore called the *prime mover* or *agonist*. The other muscles are helpers. Together all these muscles are called *synergists* (from the Greek *syn* meaning *together* and *ergein* meaning *to work*). Before training, these muscles tend to fire at different times so the movement is not efficient. With training, the synergists all fire together making the movements more efficient and powerful (see Figure 2-5).

Skeletal Muscle

The tissue that is most obviously affected by weight training is skeletal muscle. The muscles that are attached to our bones are actually a collection of muscle cells (called *muscle fibers*) bound together by connective tissues. These connective tissues allow the muscle cells to work as a unit to produce force. The connective tissues come together at the ends of the muscles (the origin and insertion) to form the tendons that attach muscle to bone (see

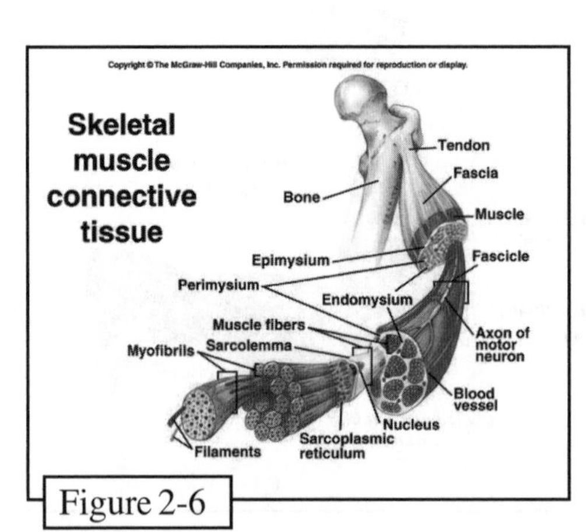

Figure 2-6

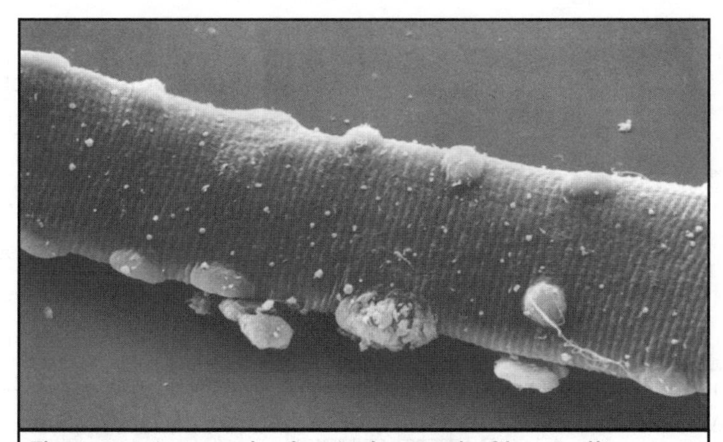

Electron micrograph of a single muscle fiber (cell) showing nuclei and satellite cells. (From Bischoff, R., "Analysis of muscle regeneration using single myofibers in culture." *Medicine and Science in Sports and Exercise*. 21(5), 5164-5172, 1989. Used with permission.

Figure 2-7

Figure 2-6). *Muscle cells (fibers)* have a unique shape dictated by their function. Rather than being spherical like a "typical cell", the muscle fiber is long and cylindrical. Unlike the cells you may remember from biology class, muscle fibers don't have one nucleus in the middle. Instead they have many *nuclei* (plural of nucleus) near the fiber's surface which push the muscle fiber's cell membrane out and form a series of irregularly occurring "bulges" along the length of the cell (see Figure 2-7). These nuclei "tell" the muscle fiber how to grow. Also, surrounding the cell on the outside of its membrane is a group of immature muscle cells called "satellite" cells, which come together to make new muscle cells (fibers) when existing fibers are damaged. Simply looking at the number of nuclei and satellite cells associated with each muscle fiber tells us that muscle cells have a tremendous ability to change their size, contractile capacity, and their number. In fact, muscle cells are so "willing" to change that exercise scientists have even adopted a word that describes this capacity, *plasticity*.

In addition to nuclei and satellite cells, the muscle fiber also has

Proteins form strands known as thick (myosin) and thin (actin) filaments.
Figure 2-8

two major types of protein, the contractile proteins and the structural proteins. The most abundant contractile proteins are myosin and actin. In the body these proteins form strands known as thick (myosin) and thin (actin) filaments (see Figure 2-8). Myosin is shaped like an arm with a long shaft and two bendable joints that act as the elbow and wrist (see Figure 2-9). At the end of the molecule are two "heads" that work like a hand to grab the actin molecule. This elbow, wrist, and hand assembly is called a crossbridge. The shafts of the myosin molecules are all joined together to form the thick filament, and the crossbridges stick out forming two double spirals that repeat every 120 degrees (see Figure 2-10). This means that there are six rows of crossbridges spiraling along the myosin filament. Running next to these rows are six actin filaments that look like two strands of pearls wrapped around each other (see Figure 2-11). When a muscle

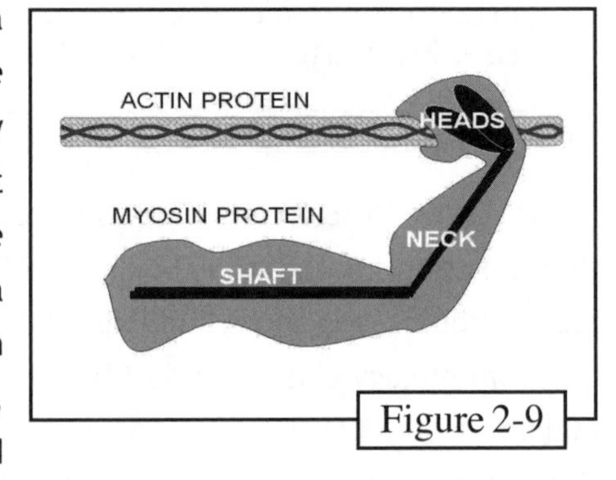

Figure 2-9

Shafts of the myosin molecules.
Figure 2-10

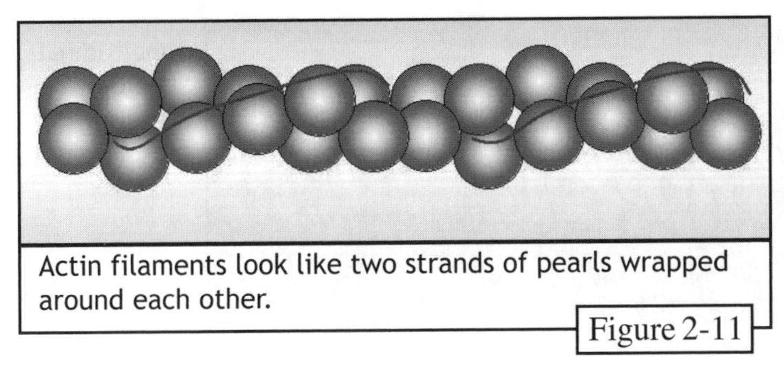

Actin filaments look like two strands of pearls wrapped around each other.

Figure 2-11

contracts, the crossbridges of the myosin filament pull the actin so it slides along the myosin. This resembles a collection of little arms all grabbing and releasing the actin at different times in a "hand-after-hand" action. The most common reason for your muscle to increase in size is for it to make more and more of these thick (myosin) and thin (actin) filaments. The process of increasing the size of a muscle fiber is call *hypertrophy*.

The myosin and actin filaments are less than two millionth of a meter long. So for a muscle cell to reach the entire length of the muscle each group of filaments must be linked together like a line of people holding hands. A group of filaments that make up a single contractile unit is called a *sarcomere*. The points where sarcomeres are linked are called *Z-lines*. When scientists want to look at a muscle they remove a portion and cut a very thin slice. This slice can either be across the muscle (a cross-sectional slice) or along its length (a longitudinal slice). When these slices are placed under a microscope and a light is shown through them they have very predictable characteristics. The cross-sectional slice (Figure 2-12) shows a collection of rounded muscle cells. This is the same type cut you would see in a delicatessen when the

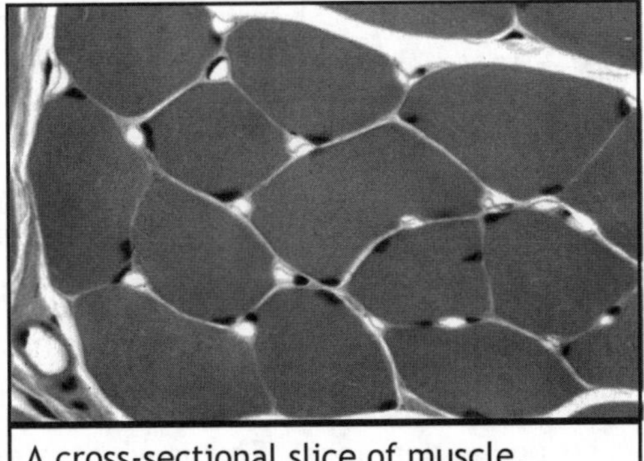

A cross-sectional slice of muscle.

Figure 2-12

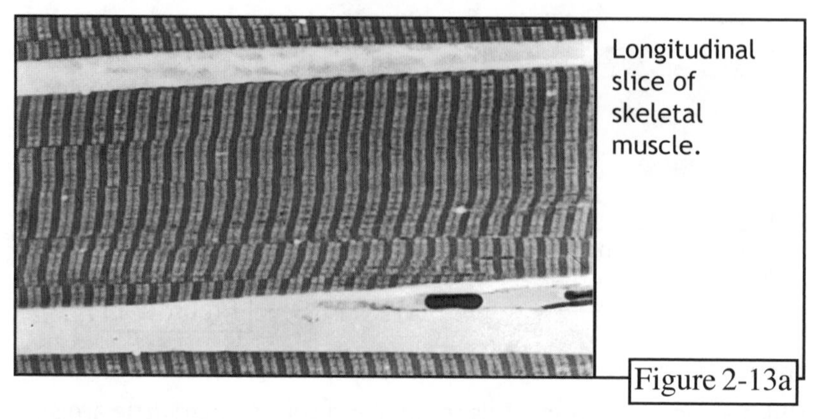

Longitudinal slice of skeletal muscle.

Figure 2-13a

butcher slices cold cuts. Between the muscle cells you can easily see the connective tissue that holds them together. The cell nuclei and satellite cells can also be clearly seen surrounding the muscle fiber (cell). The longitudinal slice (Figure 2-13a) reveals the unique repeating structure of the skeletal muscle. Figure 2-13b provides a schematic diagram of the longitudinal structure including a number of sarcomeres. To understand why a muscle looks "striped" when you look at it longitudinally, you only need to think about the thickness of the parts that make it up. The myosin filament is quite thick, while the actin filament is rather thin. The Z-lines, since they serve as both an anchor and a link, are very thick. When the light of the microscope shines through these structures the thicker structures let less light through than the thinner ones. Therefore muscle tissue has a regular pattern of light bands (called I bands) and dark bands (called A bands) which give it its striped appearance. This is why skeletal muscle is called "striated" (striped).

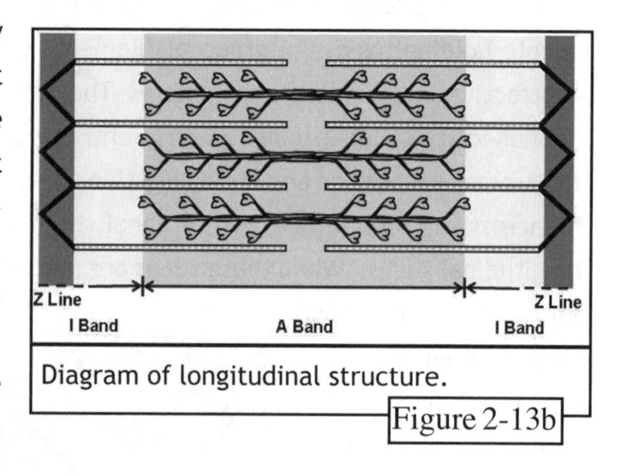

Diagram of longitudinal structure.

Figure 2-13b

When a skeletal muscle is weight-trained it can grow in a number of ways. The most common pattern of growth is for the muscle to get larger around, that is, increase its "cross-sectional area". The increase in cross-sectional area is a direct response of the muscle to the increase in load. There are two basic ways in which a muscle may increase its cross-sectional area (see figure 2-14). The first way is called hypertrophy (Greek: hyper = more, troph = food or nourishment) which we mentioned earlier. As you will remember, hypertrophy is an increase in the size of the muscle fiber. This is accomplished by an increase in thickness of the filaments and their supporting structures (like those Z-disks we spoke about). Most scientists agree that hypertrophy is the principle mechanism by which muscles grow in response to resistance training. The second mechanism by which muscles grow is called hyperplasia. This is literally an increase in the number of muscle fibers (*hyper* = more, *plasia* = a mold or form). Hyperplasia is accomplished by the activation of those satellite cells that surround the muscle cells. Satellite cells either fuse together to form new muscle fibers or enter existing muscle cells to create new muscle tissue. This is a common mechanism in response to injury, but the degree to which it is stimulated by weight training is debatable. It may be that both mechanisms are active during weight training and that the intensity of the training dictates their level of activation; however, there is little doubt that during training, hypertrophy is the dominant factor.

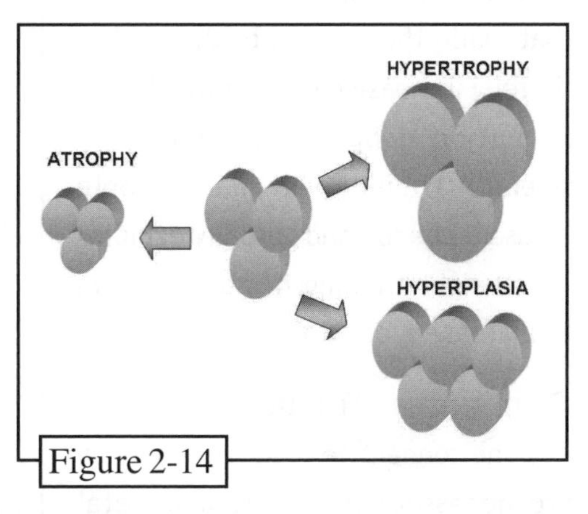

Figure 2-14

In addition to increasing cross-sectional area, resistance training can also increase the length of a skeletal muscle. Studies have shown that weight training exercises performed through a joint's full range of motion can increase the range of motion of the joint. In fact, full range of motion activities can actually add sarcomeres (those contractile units that made the stripes) to the muscle thereby increasing its length. This information debunks the myth that strength training will make people "muscle bound" and actually explains why weight-training has been shown to increase a person's flexibility.

Connective Tissue

The connective tissues of the body are necessary to maintain skeletal muscle structure, provide joint stability, and transfer force from the muscle to the skeletal system. In addition, they provide a supplementary system for force production since they store energy like an elastic band. The structures most commonly associated with connective tissue are ligaments, tendons, fascia, and protective structures such as bursa sacs and joint capsules (Figure 2-15). The major components of the connective tissues are collagen, elastin, and the ground substance or fluid in which they are held. Collagen is a triple helix (three spiraling ribbons) that provides great tensile strength and some elasticity. Elastin, as the name implies, is a much less structured tissue that is about fifteen

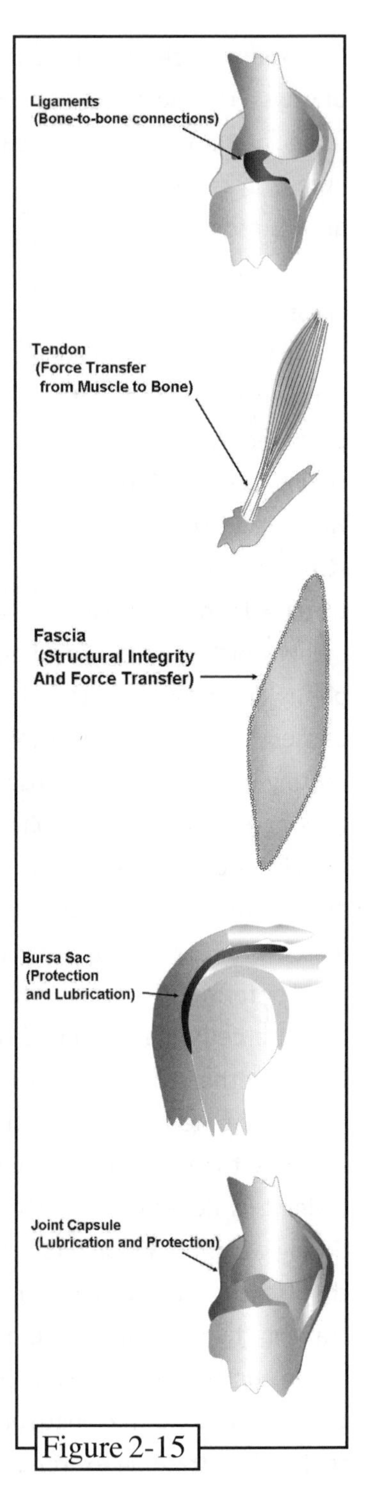

Figure 2-15

times more "stretchable" than collagen and therefore provides more compliance and elastic rebound. The ground substance, composed mainly of proteoglycans (protein and sugar complexes) and glycosaminoglycans (amino acid and sugar complexes), acts as both a support medium and lubricating system for the structural proteins. Full range of motion weight training will strengthen and elongate connective tissue. In addition, weight training, especially techniques that incorporate a deceleration (braking) phase, can increase the capacity of the muscles and tendons to store and use elastic energy. Both the increase in strength and the increase in elasticity have important implications. Strengthening connective tissue, especially during the early phases of training can reduce the level of injury and soreness commonly associated with training. Increasing the ability of the tissues to store elastic energy reduces the cost of doing an activity and therefore improves performance. In fact, pre-stretching a muscle and tendon prior to a movement may account for up to seventy percent of the energy required to complete a movement. This storage of elastic energy prior to a movement is of such importance it has been given its own name, the *stretch-shortening* cycle (see figure 2-16). As we will see in Chapters 8, 9, and 10 we always use a *tissue adaptation phase* to increase muscle and connective tissue strength

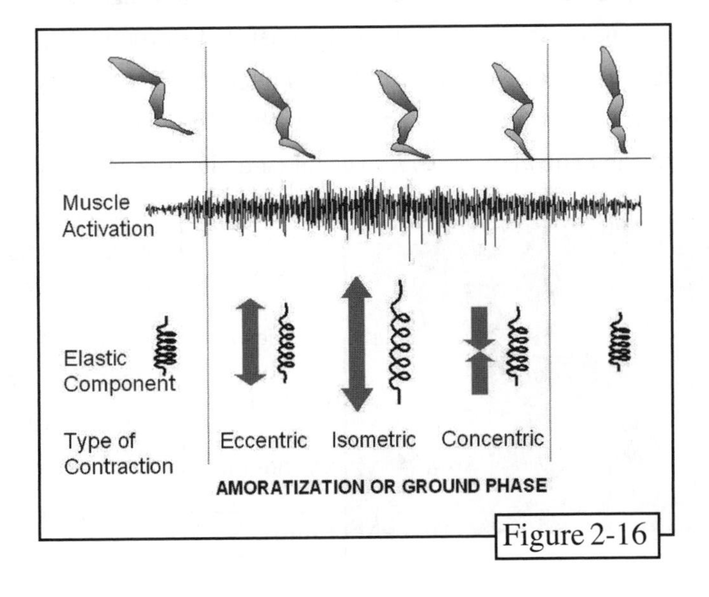

Figure 2-16

at the beginning of any workout regimen or after a prolonged layoff. In addition, our explosive training prescriptions, designed to increase power, also concentrate on connective tissue training by adding high speed deceleration movements either during the lifting or the recovery phases of the training program.

Bone

Bone is the densest tissue in the body, and as such it is often viewed as almost inanimate. In reality bone is a living connective tissue that is constantly changing. There are two types of bone, *spongy* (or *trabecular*) bone and *compact* (or *cortical*) bone (see Figure 2-17). All the bones of our body contain both types. The spongy bone is a lattice that makes up the interior of our bones. Its structure provides a balance between strength and lightness. The compact bone makes up the tough outer coat that surrounds the spongy bone. It is arranged in a series of tightly packed concentric cylinders that resemble the growth rings of a tree. These boney cylinders surround the central or *Haversian* canal (see Figure 2-18). The canal allows a space for blood vessels and the flow of bone fluids. We now know that applying a load to a bone, especially during dynamic

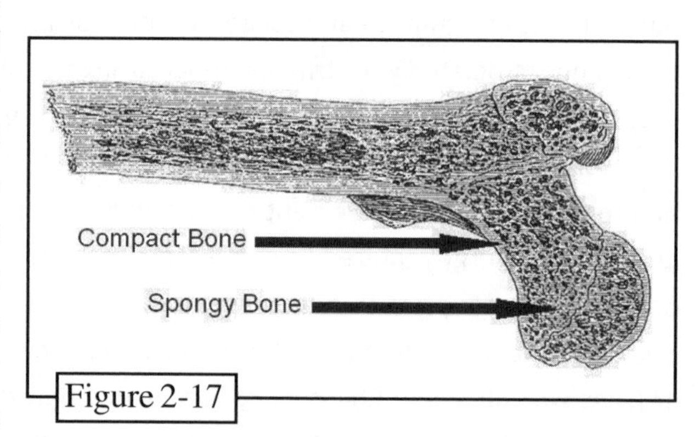

Figure 2-17

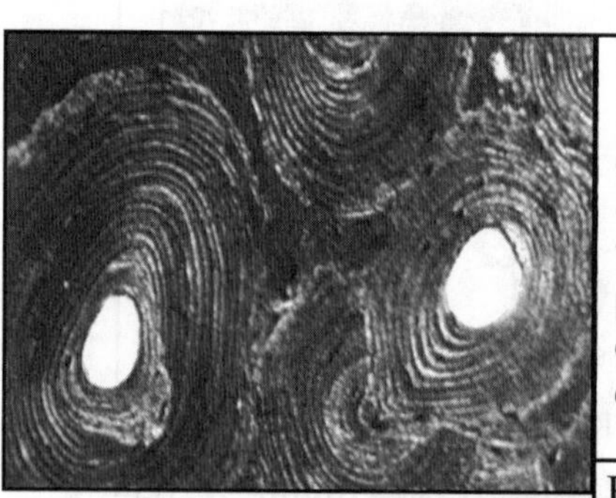
Compact bone is arranged in a series of tightly packed concentric cylinders.

Figure 2-18

movements such as weight training, causes the bone to increase in density and strength. This is especially important to women who tend to lose bone density after menopause. It is also important to everyone because the bones are the levers that support our movements, and studies have shown that bone strength improves as muscle strength increases.

The Energy Systems

Most of us are familiar with the common terms *aerobic* and *anaerobic* exercise. We also know that *aerobic* exercise (in Greek *aero* means air and *bic* is from *bio* meaning life) is exercise that uses oxygen, while *anaerobic* (in Greek *an* means not, thus "not aerobic") means exercise that does not use oxygen. However, to call an exercise aerobic or anaerobic is a mistake. The energy systems of the body don't go on and off like light switches. All the systems are running all the time. There are four systems and they run in a *continuum* or sequence (see Figure 2-19). As we do specific activities we "slide" along this continuum using one system to a greater extent than the others. For example, the most powerful, and therefore, the

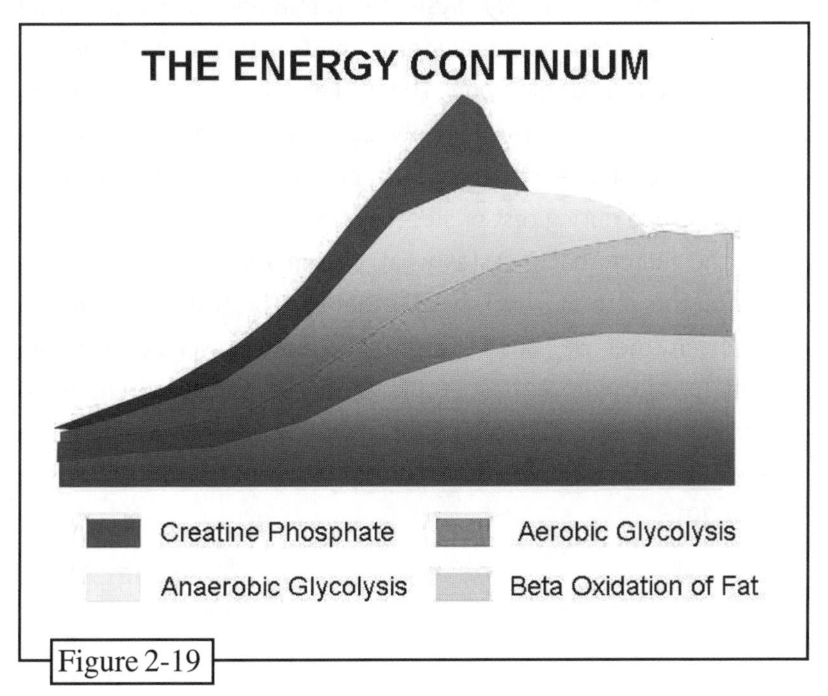

Figure 2-19

fastest system is the *phosphagen* system and its dominant fuel is *Creatine Phosphate*. During explosive movements like Olympic Lifting, throwing a ball, discus or shot-put, or serving a tennis ball, this system predominates. This does not mean the other systems turn off, it just means they can't produce energy fast enough to be very important.

The next system is *anaerobic glycolysis*. We have already defined anaerobic (without oxygen). *Glycolysis* is made up of two Greek roots *glyco* meaning "sugar" and *lysis* meaning "to break down". So *anaerobic glycolysis* is the system that breaks down sugar without using oxygen. It's not that we don't have oxygen to use, it's just that when we need energy quickly we don't have time to break down the sugar using oxygen, since this requires more steps and therefore more time than the anaerobic breakdown. It also takes some time to transport and replenish the oxygen once it is used. Examples of activities where *anaerobic glycolysis* may be the dominant system would be short sprints or gymnastic events. The next system is *aerobic glycolysis*. If *anaerobic glycolysis* means breaking down sugar without using oxygen, then *aerobic glycolysis* means to break down sugar using oxygen. This system predominates in most distance events like 5k runs, marathons, and triathlons. The final energy system is the breakdown of fat using oxygen, commonly known as *beta oxidation* due to the steps that initiate it. This system predominates at very low activity levels and during rest or sleep.

So the factor that dictates what system will be used is power output or the rate at which work is done. The faster the rate of work, the further we "slide" toward the more powerful anaerobic systems (*phospagens* and *anaerobic glycolysis*) the lower the work rate or more relaxed the activity the greater the dependence on the more oxidative systems (*aerobic glycolysis* and *beta oxidation*) (see figure 2-20).

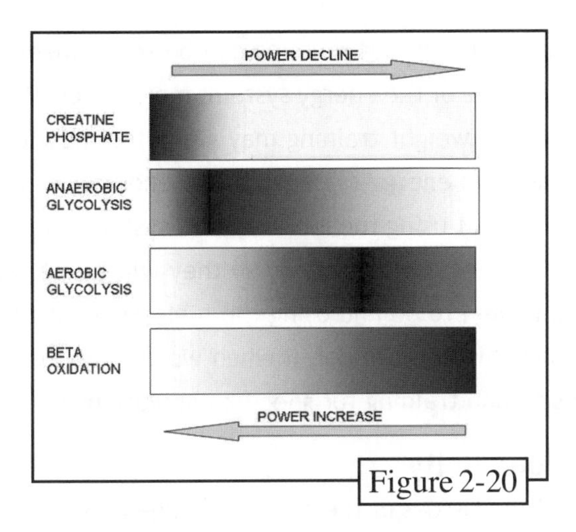

Figure 2-20

The "So What?" of Energy Systems

Many scientists compare the human body to a machine. Using this analogy, if we change the parts on the machine, we can change what the machine does. For example, a car with a large engine and light body can go very fast. A truck with an even bigger engine but with a heavy body built to withstand damage, can't go as fast, but can pull very heavy loads. The human machine is similar. As you will see in the sections below, we can actually change the structures of the body to make them stronger and faster through training. But we can do much more. Just like engines, different types of muscle cells have structural differences that make them better at doing certain things and cause them to prefer one fuel over another. With proper training we can re-engineer our muscles so that they make these changes we want.

Let's look at an example. A high performance sports car, built for speed, uses high-octane fuel. A compact car, built for economy, uses regular fuel. And a big tractor trailer, built to move large loads over long distances, uses diesel fuel. If we change the parts of these vehicles, for example, If we put a high performance engine in the economy compact, the car will run more like a sports car and it will also burn the high-octane fuel that a sports car uses. Just like a car, the fibers that make up our muscles can be re-engineered through training to use some of the energy systems more efficiently than others. So, explosive weight training may make the muscles better at using the anaerobic energy systems, while endurance training may make them better at using the more aerobic systems. In this way we can change the engines of our body so they will be better at doing what we want them to do and using the fuels we want them to use. We will discuss this in more detail when we look at the chapter on program design and training for specific populations.

Training Specificity

For any of the tissues of the body to change they must be given a reason or *stimulus* that demands that change occurs. In the case of exercise training this stimulus is called an *overload.* One of the most basic concepts in exercise science is the *Overload Principle.* The *Overload Principle* states that for a tissue or a system of the body to change, an outside stimulus greater than the body's normal activity level must be applied. If the correct level of *overload* is applied, the body reacts to the overload by *adaptation. Adaptation* is simply the body re-engineering its energy systems and tissues so they can handle the overload. It's sort of like putting heavier shock absorbers on a car or truck so it can go off-road or thicker cables and supports on a bridge so it can handle heavier traffic.

Since the body is so good at re-engineering itself, it only makes the changes necessary to answer the overload given. So we can say the change or *adaptation* made by the body is *specific* to the *overload* applied. This is known as *exercise* or *training specificity.* You see examples of training specificity every day but probably don't pay much attention to them. A simple example is to look at two athletes, a bodybuilder and a distance runner (see Figure 2-21). Even though both may train for the same number of hours each week, they look nothing alike. This is because the bodybuilder's muscles and energy systems have adapted to handling heavy loads, while the distance runner's muscles only have to carry his or her body weight and,

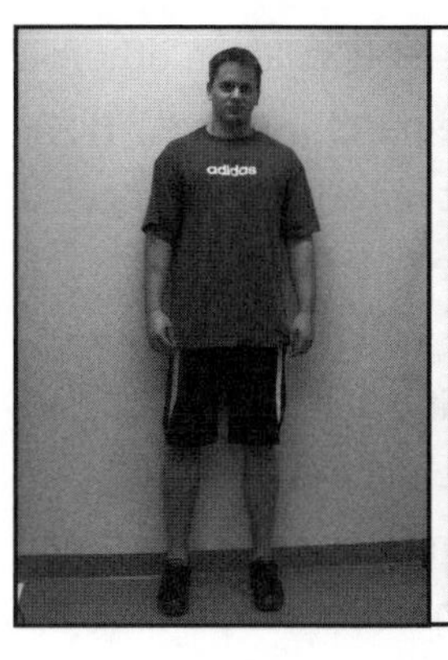

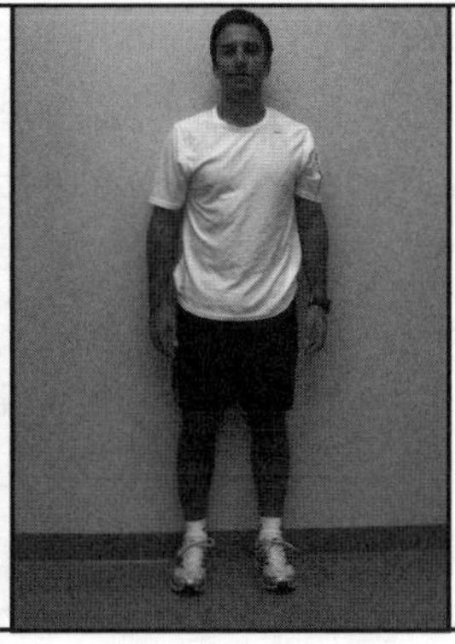

The muscles of a body builder adapt differently from the muscles of a distance runner.

Figure 2-21

therefore, have been redesigned to allow the more efficient use of oxygen. Once we understand this principle, we're well on our way to understanding how to develop specific training programs designed to meet our needs and goals and those of the people who seek our help. There are a number of different types of specificity. We will describe the two major types in this text. One is *bioenergetic* (Greek *bio* = living; and *energetic* = having to do with the energy systems) specificity and the other is *biomechanical* (*bio* = living; *mechanical* = the physics of motion and forces) specificity. In this chapter we will look at *bioenergetic* specificity, and in Chapter 3 we'll examine *biomechanical* specificity. Even though we use these two different classifications, the body can no more separate bioenergetics from biomechanics than a car can separate its engine from its transmission, axles, or wheels. We make this separation so it will be easier to examine the diverse changes the body can make as a result of the different training stimuli applied.

Bioenergetic Specificity

As we stated earlier, the skeletal muscle cell is like a living engine whose sole purpose is to move our bones. Not all cells are exactly the same, however, just like not all people are exactly the same. Most of us have the same basic parts, a head, arms, a torso, and legs, but we all look a bit different and have different strengths and weaknesses depending on the nature of these parts. Some of us may have stronger arms, some faster legs, some may be a bit smarter, others a bit larger, all dependent on the nature of the parts we have. However, we can change these parts. We can get bigger and stronger if we weight-train. We can get smarter if we read and study. We can get more flexible if we stretch. Our muscle cells are just like us, they have the same parts, but they're just a bit different. Just as we can cause different changes in our bodies depending on the things we do, we can make different changes in our muscle cells which can make them better at doing one thing or another.

Figure 2-22 shows the inside of a muscle cell with all its parts. It's a fairly complicated machine. Although training can change all of these parts, we're only going to concentrate on a few of the most important ones. We will concentrate on these parts since they provide energy and are therefore the ones related to *bioenergetic specificity*. The part that comes to mind when you speak about energy production in a cell is the "powerhouse of the cell" or *mitochondrion* (singular of mitochondria). This is the part of the cell responsible for aerobic energy production (metabolism). You can also produce energy outside the mitochondria in the cytoplasm (*cyto* = cell, *plasm* = fluid). Anaerobic metabolism takes place in the cytoplasm (see figure 2-23). Both of these areas contain special chemicals called *enzymes*. Each group of enzymes is responsible for breaking down different fuels in different ways to

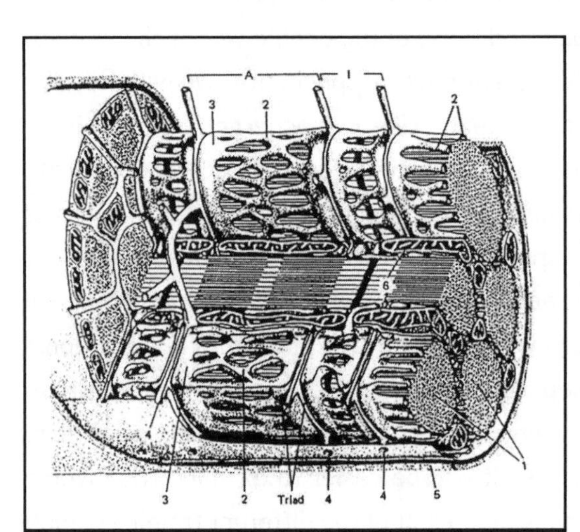

The interior parts of a muscle cell.

Figure 2-22

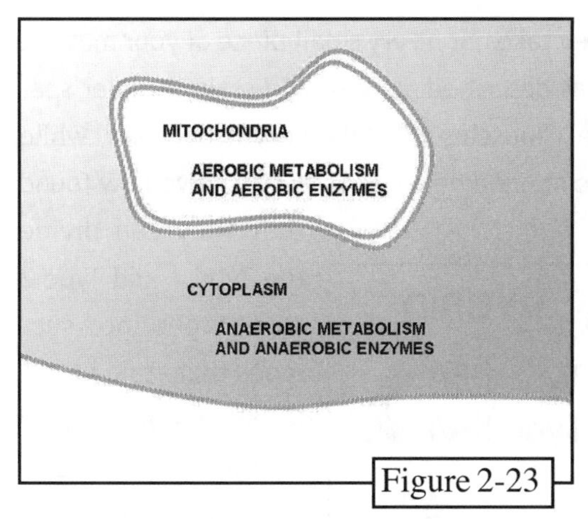

Figure 2-23

provide energy. So if your body has more mitochondria it has more aerobic enzymes. Therefore it is better at using oxygen and doing things for longer time periods. When we train by running or walking long distances or even by weight training by moving from one machine to another with limited rest when we weight train, we are targeting the aerobic systems and therefore increasing the number and size of our *mitochondria* so they can hold more *aerobic enzymes*. This is *bioenergetic* training that concentrates on *aerobic* improvements. On the other hand, if we train mainly by running sprints or by lifting heavy weights, we target the more *anaerobic* systems and therefore make the *anaerobic enzymes* more numerous and more effective. The specific changing of cell parts to make the cell better at using one energy system compared to another is *bioenergetic* specificity. We will look at how this is applied during weight training in our chapter on program design for specific populations.

Skeletal Muscle Fiber Types and Bioenergetic Specificity

Many of you have probably heard that your muscles have at least two muscle fiber types, fast twitch and slow twitch. Scientists now have given these fiber types numbers rather than names. Slower contracting muscle fibers are usually *Type 1*, while faster contracting fibers are *Type 2*. So how do these scientists distinguish between the Type 1 and Type 2 fibers? They do it by staining a very special enzyme that is part of the myosin molecule we described earlier in this chapter. That enzyme is called *myosin ATPase* and it determines how fast the crossbridge arms we described earlier will pull the actin ropes.

Scientists know that if they take out a very small piece of your muscle, cut it cross-sectionally (as described above), and stain it under special conditions, the Type 1 muscles will take very little stain, while the Type 2 muscle will be stained heavily. Scientists have now found that they can divide the Type 1 and Type 2 fiber types into subtypes that stain at different shades. So, we now have four muscle fiber types (Type 1, 2A, 2D, and 2B) and six hybrid fiber types (Type 1/2A, 2A/1, 2AD/2DA, 2DA/2AD, 2DB/2BD, 2BD/2DB) as pictured in Figure 2-24. The hybrid types contain myosin proteins from both the pure fiber types listed and the one listed first indicated the pure fiber type the hybrid is most like. For example, a Type 2DA/2AD contains proteins from the pure Type 2D and Type 2A fiber types, but is more like a Type 2D than a Type 2A.

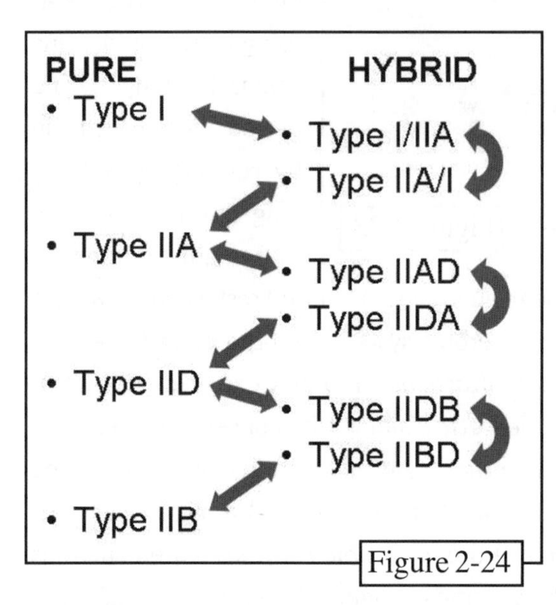

Figure 2-24

Just as the energy systems form a continuum from aerobic to anaerobic metabolism, so the muscle types form a continuum. And just as training can change the structures within your muscle so that it uses one energy system better than another, you can also change your muscle's fiber type. In fact, scientists now know that training causes very specific changes in skeletal muscle fiber types. Training, regardless of the type, always causes Type 2D fibers to change to Type 2DA or 2AD fibers. More aerobic training appears to encourage further change from Type 2DA to Type 2AD and may eventually cause the fibers to change to Type 2AD to type 2A/1 or even Type 1 (see Figure 2-24). So you can actually change the fibers types in your muscles by changing your training methods. This is another reason why designing the proper training program is so important. If you want to make specific changes in your body, or if you have special needs that require specific changes (atrophy or muscle imbalances due to injury or disease, specific joints that must have greater strength or endurance for a work task or sport), then programs must be designed to target the goals and needs of that person. Simply stated, when it comes to weight training, "one size does not fit all". The program must be tailored to the results you want. Chapter 9 will provide the information necessary to do this by providing specific programs to meet the needs of different populations and explaining the logic behind their development.

Delayed Onset of Muscle Soreness (DOMS)

We should not leave this chapter on the physiology of training without addressing the reason for the soreness often experienced after a high-intensity training bout. Any time you lift weights, or do any exercise that stresses your muscles and connective tissues, you will cause some degree of microscopic damage. Although you can't see the injury, you can certainly feel it, and you usually feel it one or two days after the exercise is actually performed. We've all felt that "next day" soreness after training. In fact it's so common it's even been named. It is called delayed onset muscle soreness or simply DOMS. Many people will tell you it's caused by lactic acid, but as we saw earlier in this chapter, lactic acid is a by-product of metabolism that is removed during recovery and returns to baseline values within

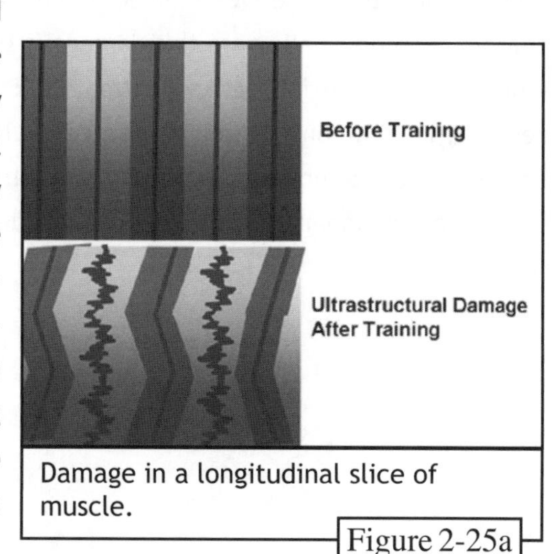

Damage in a longitudinal slice of muscle.

Figure 2-25a

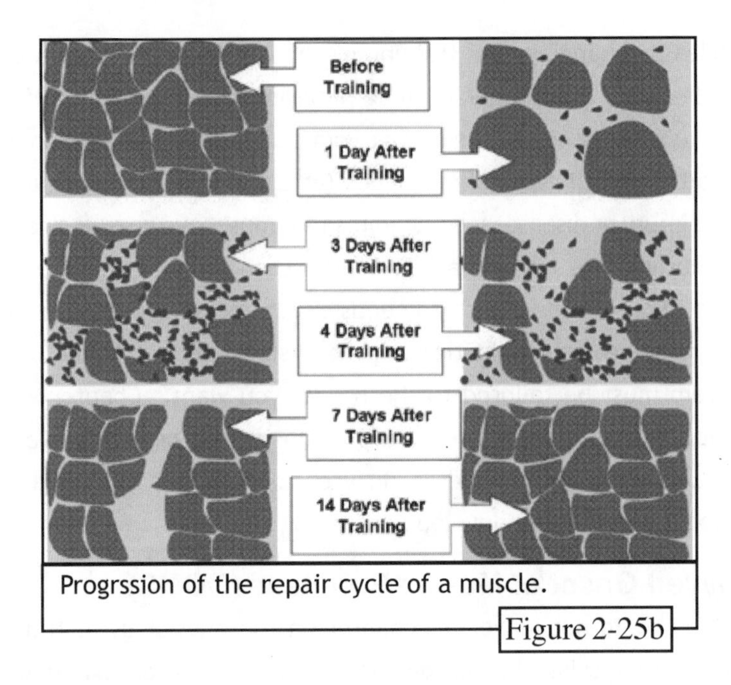

Progrssion of the repair cycle of a muscle.

Figure 2-25b

minutes after an exercise is completed. DOMS is actually a reaction to injury. Just as your finger would swell up and hurt if you hit it with a hammer, your muscle swells up and hurts when you damage it with training. Figure 2-25a shows you this damage in a longitudinal slice of muscle and Figure 2-25b shows you a series of pictures of a muscle going through the damage and repair cycle. As you can see from the picture, fluid builds between the cells and they swell. The best thing that you can do to alleviate this damage is the typical response you would make to any injury like a sprain, RICE. RICE is an acronym for rest (R), ice (I), compression (C), and elevation (E). The rest allows the muscle to repair itself, while the ice, compression, and elevation reduce the secondary damage that occurs due to swelling and inflammation.

Chapter

3

Mechanics of Weight Training

Bones and Joints

Muscles move the bones of the body. The bones are functional levers that pivot on one another forming joints. There are a number of different types of joints. Some joints are fused together so they allow very little movement like the suture joints in your skull, while others provide different degrees of freedom. The most common moveable joints in the skeletal system are presented in Figure 3-1. They include sliding joints (*arthroidial*), concave joints (condyloid), saddle joints (*sellar*), hinge joints (*ginglymus*), ball-and-socket joints (*enartroidial*) and pivot joints (*trochoidal*). The importance of the joints

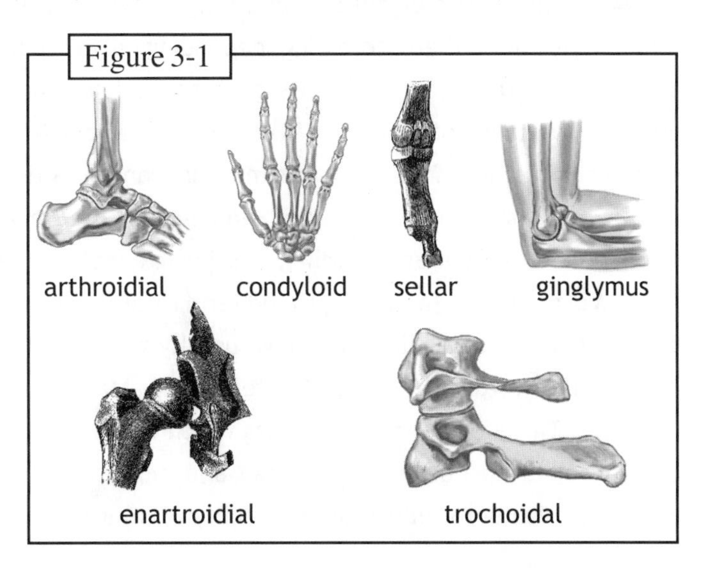

is that they control the planes of motion through which we move. Since a bone needs a muscle to move it, the joints also dictate the shapes of the muscles about them. Muscles may have a tubular shape (*longitudinal*), a spindle shape (*fusiform*), a fan shape (*radiate*), or a single (*unipennate*) or double (*bipennate*) wing shape (see Figure 3-2) depending on the joint it moves, the bones available for attachment, and the movements it is designed to perform.

Figure 3-2

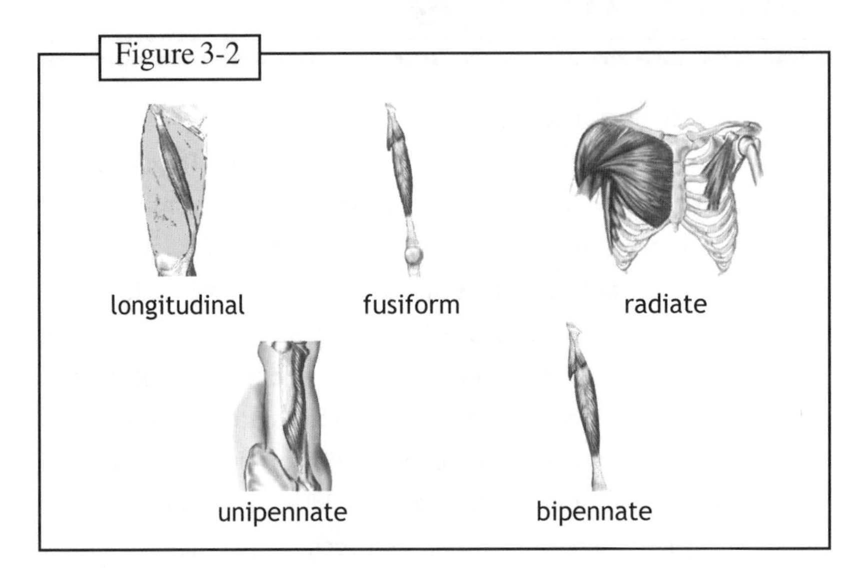

While the shapes of muscles and range of motion of the joints may or may not be that interesting, depending on your point of view, they are important factors in lifting. When a joint can move in a great many planes of motion it is very versatile, but it is also very unstable. This means it allows us to move in many directions, but the joint is highly susceptible to injury and needs a great many muscles to provide movement and stability. A prime example is the shoulder joint. Most of us are familiar with the term rotator cuff, not because of its versatility as a joint (which we usually take for granted), but because the words "rotator cuff" are usually attached to the word "injury". Therefore, lifting exercises which involve ball and socket or pivot joints must be done cautiously, and increases in load must be applied gradually to reduce the possibility of injury.

Joints and Associated Movements

As noted in the section above, the more complex a joint the greater the number of movement patterns it can produce. These movement patterns are often used to describe the exercises performed during weight training and other activities and are therefore of interest. Nearly every joint in the body is capable of flexion and extension. Flexion is the closing of a joint angle or, simply, when one bone gets closer to another. Extension is the opening of the joint angle or when the bones move further apart. The joints in which it is easiest to visualize flexion and extension are the hinge joints like the elbow and knee (Figure 3-3). However, other joints can also perform these actions. For example, Figure 3-4 shows trunk flexion and extension, respectively.

Figure 3-3

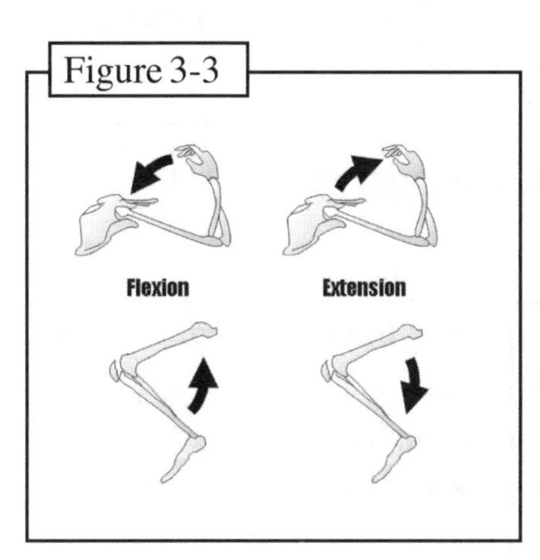

Figure 3-4

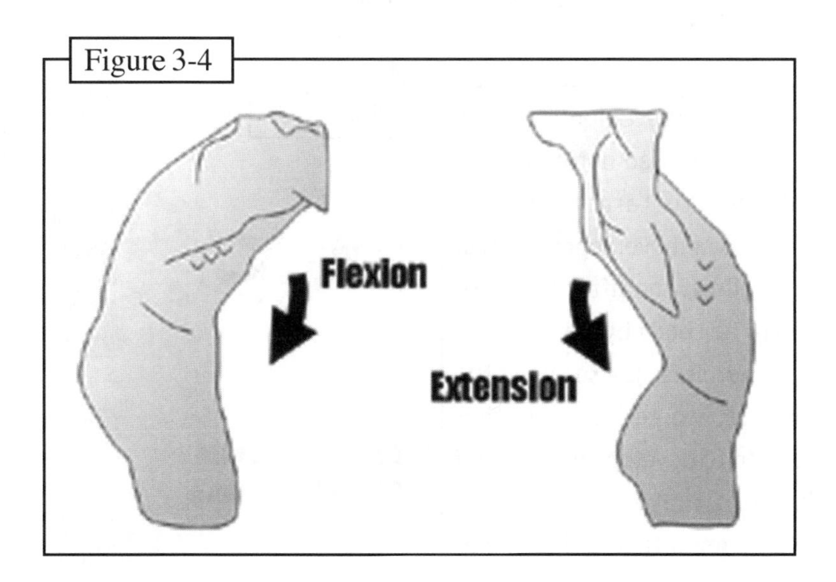

A second set of movement patterns often associated with lifting are adduction and abduction. These movements are commonly depicted during movements of the shoulder and hip joints. Figure 3-5 shows hip adduction and abduction, two common exercises done in the weight room.

Figure 3-5

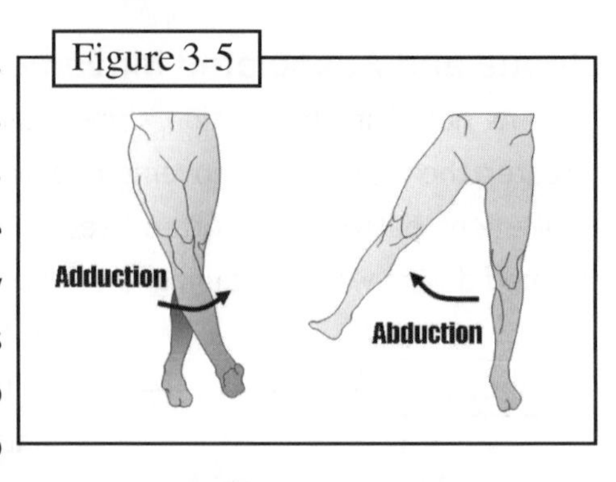

A third movement often used during training is rotation. Rotation is common to ball-and-socket, sliding, saddle, and pivot joints. Common examples are the rotation of the shoulders and the hips commonly seen during throwing activities (Figure 3-6) and the internal and external rotation of the shoulder (Figure 3-7).

Figure 3-6

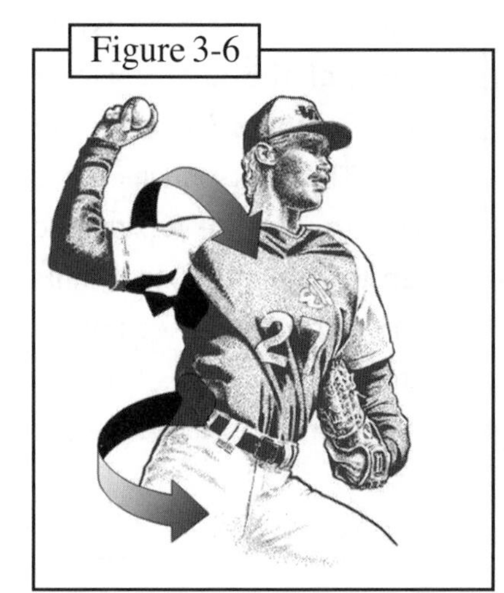

These movements can be selectively used during weight training to target specific muscles or movement patterns. This allows the lifter to sculpt his or her body by using different exercises. It also allows the athlete, worker, or any other person to develop strength and power using specific movements important to his or her sport or activity.

Figure 3-7

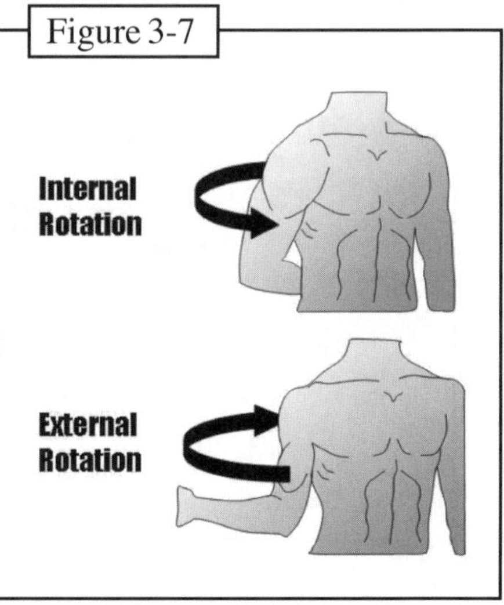

Joints and Targeting Specific Muscles or Movements

One of the major concerns in resistance training is targeting specific muscles or movements for either performance or aesthetics. This is one aspect of what is called *biomechanical specificity*. Biomechanics is the study of the physical laws governing the movement of the body, while specificity indicates that the body will adapt in a unique way in response to the training stimulus provided. Muscles like the quadriceps femoris (*quadriceps* = four heads, *femoris* = femur or thigh bone) or biceps femoris (*biceps* = two heads), which attach to a hinge joint like the knee, are easiest to target. Since hinge joints have a limited range of motion, the muscles that move them are usually straight or spindle-shaped and pull along a single plane.

Other muscles, which are attached to joints capable of more complex movements, often have multiple angles of pull. Different sections of these muscles can be targeted by moving the weights in different planes of motion. A common example of this is the pectoralis major (pectoralis = breast) or chest muscle. As we will see in Chapter 5, one of the most common exercises used to target this muscle is the bench press. The bench press can be performed on a flat bench, inclined bench, or declined bench. Depending on the angle of the bench, different parts of the pectoralis can be targeted. A simple way to know the portion of the muscle being targeted by an exercise is by drawing a line from the starting point of the exercise movement to the end point. This line or *vector* then points toward the section of the muscle being targeted. This *vector of muscle utilization* is illustrated for both pushing and pulling movements in Figure 3-8. Chapter 5 will describe a number of exercises that work these multipennate muscles and indicate which ones target specific areas of those muscles.

Figure 3-8

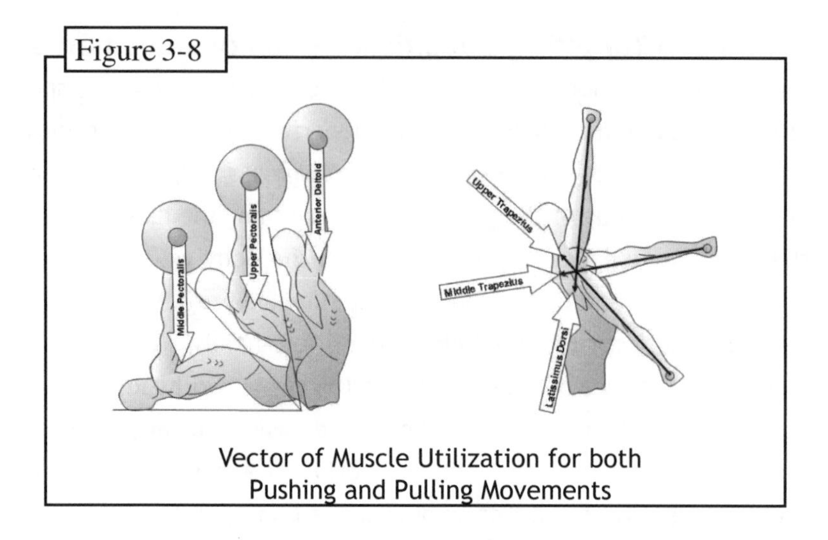

Vector of Muscle Utilization for both Pushing and Pulling Movements

Muscles and Tendons: Making the Connection

As you will recall from Chapter 2 muscles are made up of many individual muscle fibers (or muscle cells) all wrapped together in connective tissue. That connective tissue then comes together at the end of the muscle to form a tendon. Tendons connect muscles to bones (see Figure 3-9). As we noted in Chapter 2, many scientists model the human body like a machine with the muscle as the engine and the bones as the components used to transfer the energy to other objects. In order to keep this machine in balance, keep it under control, and hold it together, muscles are arranged in opposing groups. We may use different terms to describe a muscle group depending on what it is doing at any specific time. For example, if a muscle is causing a movement to happen, like a bicep brachii moving your arm when you're flexing your elbow, that muscle is called *the prime mover* or *agonist* (Greek: *agonistikos* = make a

Figure 3-9

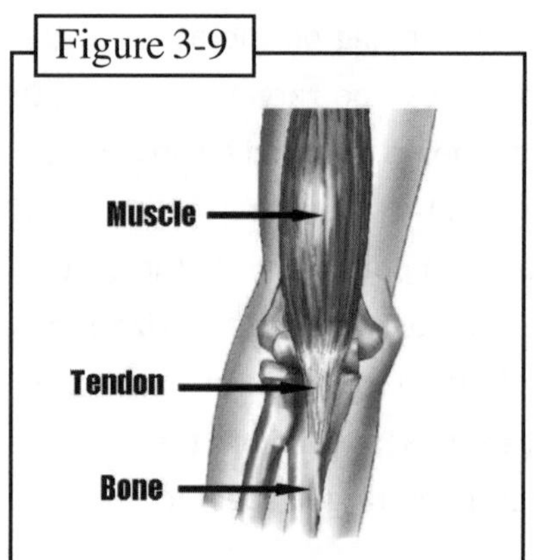

contest). The muscle on the other side that is controlling the movement and maintaining the integrity of the joint is called the *antagonist* or literally the muscle working against (*anti-*) the agonist. The other muscles that are helping with the movement are called *synergists* (Greek: *syn-* = together; *ergon* = work) or *accessory* muscles (see Figure 3-10).

Figure 3-10

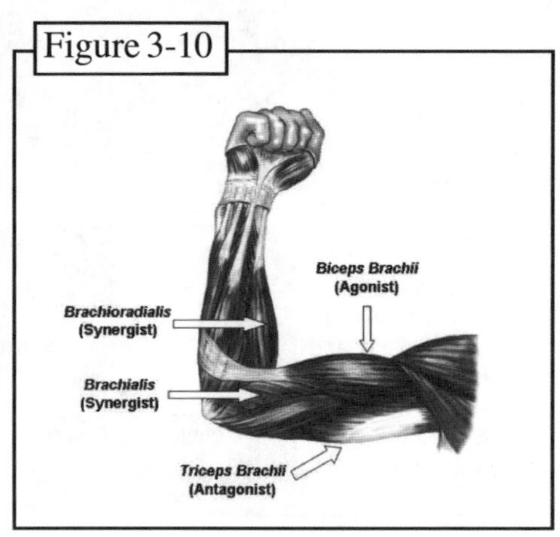

Bones as Levers

As we stated above, muscles are the machines that move the bones of our body. These bones act as levers so we can make movements. If we look around us there are all kinds of levers. For example, children playing on a see-saw are using a lever, the laborer moving a wheelbarrow filled with cement is using a lever, and the baseball player swinging his bat is using a lever. All levers have five basic parts: (1) the fulcrum, (2) the force, (3) the resistance, (4) the force arm, and (5) the resistance arm (see Figure 3-11). The fulcrum is the pivot point of the lever. The force is the point at which an outside force pushes or pulls on the lever. The resistance is the point at which the weight of the object being moved is centered.

Figure 3-11

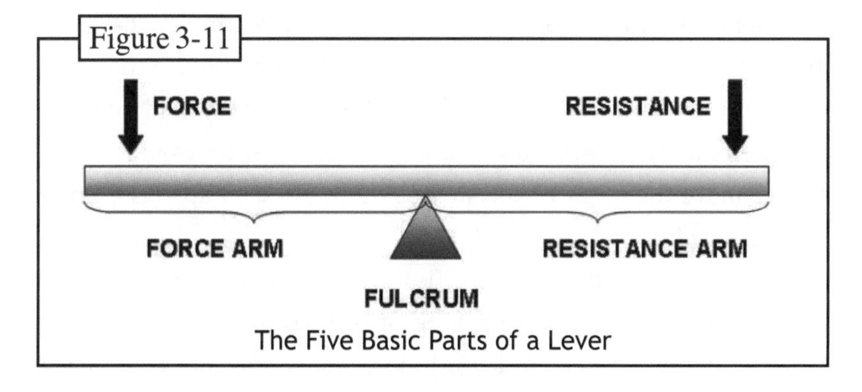

The Five Basic Parts of a Lever

Figure 3-12A

When the distance between the small rock and his hands (the force arm) is longer than the distance from the small rock to the large rock (the resistance arm), the lever makes him stronger.

Figure 3-12B

When the small rock is close to his hands, the force arm is short and the resistance arm is long. Using this lever he will be unable to move the stone.

The force arm is the distance from the force to the fulcrum, and the resistance arm is the distance from the resistance to the fulcrum.

The longer the force arm compared to the resistance arm the easier it is to move the resistance. We all know this, but we usually don't think of it in these terms. For example, if a man wants to move a large rock he can use a long board and a smaller rock. To do so he puts the board (the lever arm) under the rock he wants to move (the resistance). He then puts the small rock (the fulcrum) very close to the large one, goes to the other end and pushes (the force) and the large rock moves. This is because the distance between the small rock and his hands (the force arm) is longer than the distance from the small rock to the large rock (the resistance arm) so the lever makes him stronger (see Figure 3-12A). If he were to place the small rock close to his hands (Figure 3-12B) the force arm would be short and the resistance arm would be long; therefore, he would not be able to move the large stone. In fact we would say that this is obvious since he has no "leverage".

Another way to design a lever is to make the resistance arm long and the force arm short. This type of lever is made for speed and range of motion (see Figure 3-13A). An example is an oar on a racing shell (boat). The distance from the oars handle (force) to the oar lock (fulcrum) is short, while the distance from the oar lock to the blade (resistance) is long. This lever is designed to provide long strokes and to move the boat through the water quickly (see Figure 3-13B).

Figure 3-13A

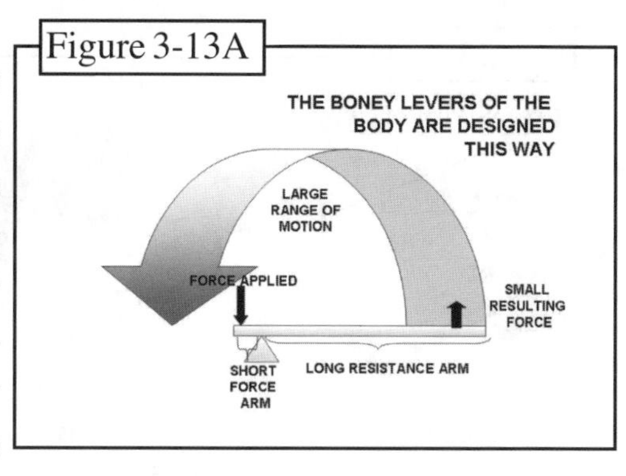

Figure 3-13B

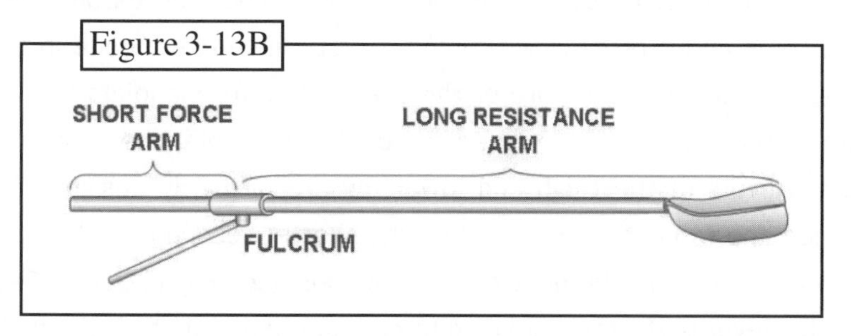

There are three classes of levers, class 1, class 2, and class 3. They are named by the relative positions of the parts (see Figure 3-14). Class 1 is the lever we think of most often when we think of a lever. The fulcrum is in the middle, the force is at one end and the resistance is at the other. As noted above, it can be used to increase force, speed, or range of motion depending on where you put the fulcrum. The class 2 lever has the fulcrum at one end, the force at the other and the weight in the middle. The best example of this is a wheelbarrow. As you can see, the force arm is always longer than the resistance arm in this lever because of the positions of the components. So this lever is only designed for increasing force. The class 3 lever has the fulcrum at one end, the resistance at the other and the force in the middle. In this class of lever the resistance arm is always longer than the force arm, so it is designed only to increase speed and range of motion. An example of this type of lever is a baseball bat.

Figure 3-14

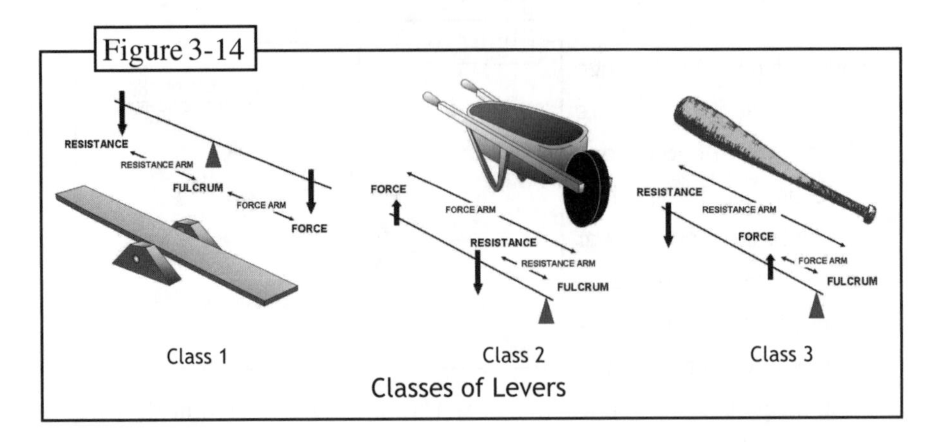

Classes of Levers

The concept of levers is important for a number of reasons when we think about resistance training. First, since every bone in the body is a lever, the nature of the levers at different joints tells us what those joints are designed to do. For example, the long third class levers of the thigh and lower leg are primarily designed for speed and range of motion, while the shorter second class lever at the ankle is designed for strength or support (see Figure 3-15). Second, a lever performs best when force is applied to it at a right angle (perpendicular to the lever arm), so most of the long bones of the body will produce their greatest force at the point in their range of motion where the muscles pull at a right angle on the bones. At the ends of the range of motion, force production tends to be lower (see Figure 3-16). This change in mechanical efficiency throughout the

Figure 3-15

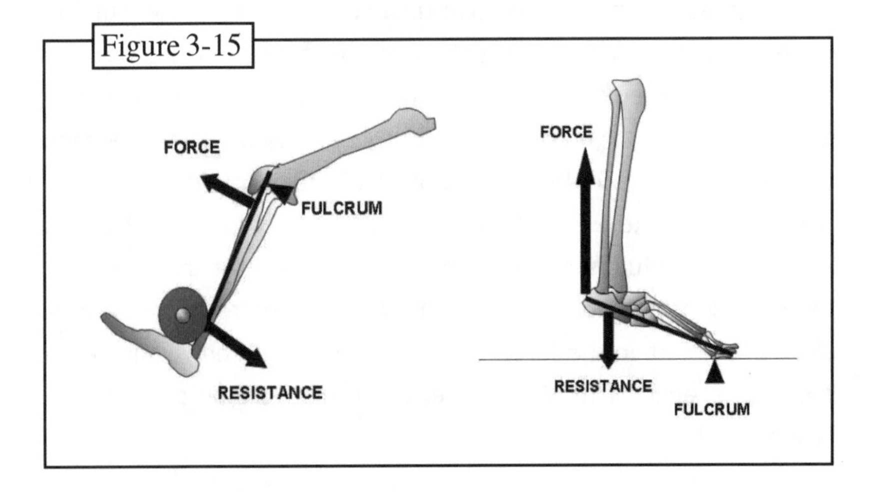

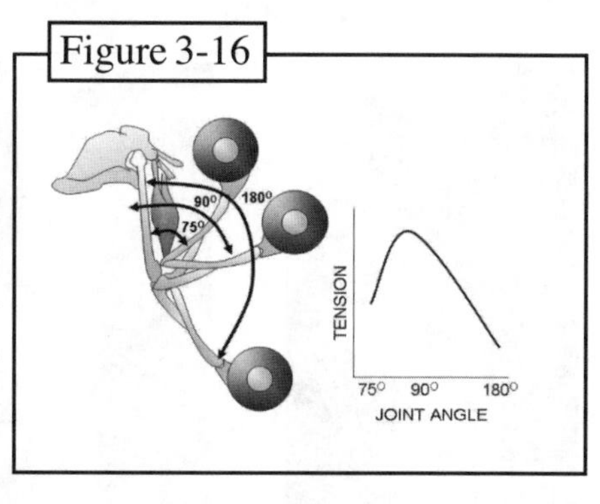

Figure 3-16

range of motion means that we can only train using loads equivalent to those we can move at the weakest point in our range of motion; unless we "cheat" either by using other muscles to begin the movement, or we utilize machines specifically designed to accommodate for changes in leverage throughout the range of motion (see Chapter 4). Third, most weight training machines have lever arms that pivot around a bearing. To use these machines most effectively and reduce the probability of injury the joint being trained should be in line with the pivot point of the machine.

Types of Muscle Contractions

During weight training muscles go through three types of contractions: isometric, concentric, and eccentric (see Figure 3-17). At the beginning of any lift the weight is stationary. Therefore, the

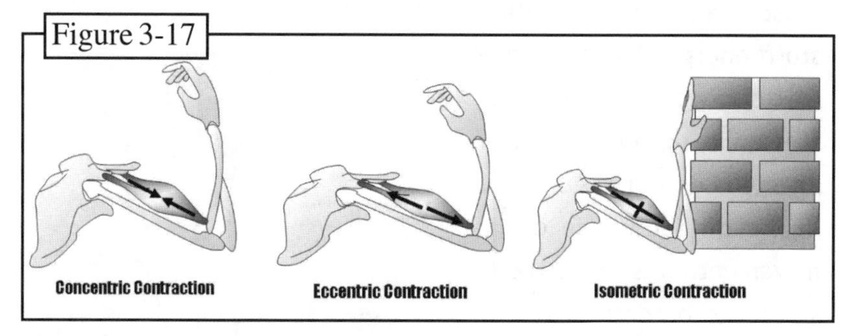

Figure 3-17

muscle must move the weight from its static position. It is at this instant, when there is no apparent movement in either the weight or in the joint, that the muscle is experiencing an isometric contraction. In fact, the term isometric means *same length (iso* = same; *metric* = length). There is also a short isometric contraction between the lifting (concentric) and lowering (eccentric) (Figure 3-18) portions of the lift. Although there is no "apparent movement" of the

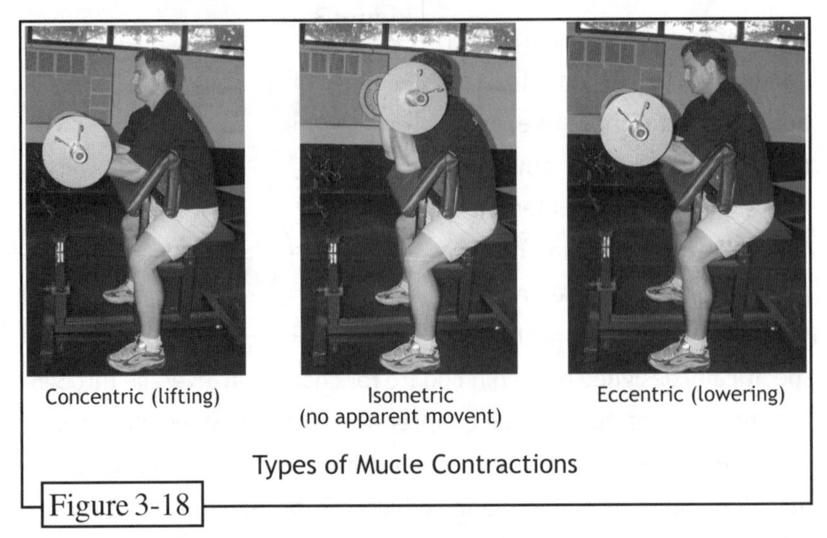

Concentric (lifting) Isometric (no apparent movent) Eccentric (lowering)

Types of Mucle Contractions

Figure 3-18

joint or lengthening of the muscle, microscopic studies have shown that the muscle and tendon actually do change length with changes in load during isometric contractions even though the joint angle is held fairly constant. This change in length is caused by the muscle and tendon stretching, just like an elastic band, to compensate for the change in weight (see Figure 3-19). Just like an elastic band, the muscle and tendon will store energy that can be used during the movement. This ability to store and use energy is one of the most important factors in our movement. It is called the *stretch-shortening cycle* and we use it every time we move. We will discuss it in more detail at the end of this chapter.

Figure 3-19

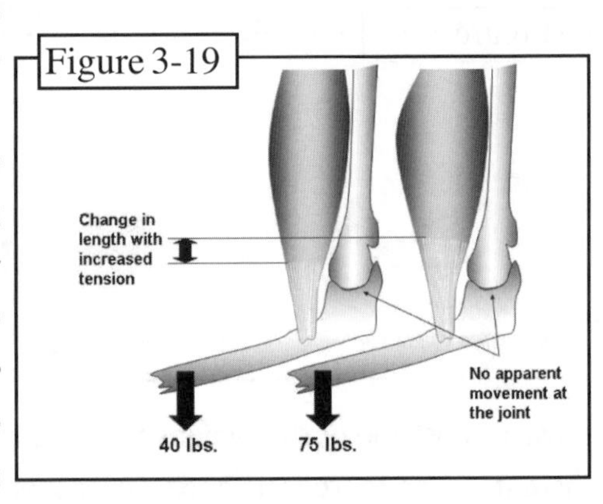

A weight training movement can begin with either a concentric or eccentric contraction. If the lift starts by lowering the weight, like a free-weight bench press or squat (see Chapter 5), the first movement is an eccentric contraction. If the lift starts by raising the weight, like an arm curl or leg extension, the first movement is a concentric contraction. Since most of us think of concentric contractions when we think of lifting, and since the majority of the machine lifts we perform begin with concentric contractions, we'll describe this type of contraction first.

A concentric contraction means that the muscle is shortening. The word is taken from two Latin roots *com* which means together and *centric* meaning center. So *concentric* literally means that the parts of the muscle are coming together at the center, or the muscle itself is shortening. This normally occurs when a weight is being lifted against gravity.

The final type of contraction that your muscle can perform during weight training is an eccentric contraction. The term eccentric can be traced back to both Latin and Greek. In Latin *eccentros* means "out of the center" and in Greek two roots are combined to make the word, *ekkentros* (*ek* = out of, *kentron* = center). Looking at both these words the nature of an eccentric contraction becomes evident. If concentric means shortening of a muscle, then eccentric must mean lengthening of a muscle. This is a common occurrence any time we lower a load, whether that load be our own limb, our body, or in the case of weight training an outside load such as a dumbbell.

Muscle Specificity

Muscle specificity means that we can target the specific muscles we wish to train by using movements designed to engage those muscles. You can easily see this by looking at athletes. For example, let's compare the muscles of a male swimmer to those of a male cyclist. The male swimmer will show good size and definition in his upper body musculature, but much less development in his leg muscles. This is because, especially for males, freestyle swimming is an upper body dominated sport. For a cyclist the opposite is true. Most cyclists have excellent lower body development with limited upper body musculature. It's a simple matter of which muscles predominate during a specific movement.

In resistance training the ability to target specific muscles is even more dramatic. Many exercises are named for the muscle or muscle group they target, like the *biceps* curl, *lat* pulldown, or *shoulder* press. Bodybuilders have made a science of targeting specific muscles so that they can attain the perfect balance of size and symmetry required to dominate in their competitive events. Strength and conditioning coaches also try to target the muscles that are most important to the athletes they train based on the specific sports involved. Trainers and physical therapists often target specific muscles during resistance training to reduce the probability of injury, increase functionality, or rehabilitate muscles atrophied through disuse or injury. In Chapter 6 we will not only describe specific lifts, we will also indicate the muscles they target.

Movement Specificity

Although movement specificity may seem a lot like muscle specificity, there is a subtle yet important difference. When we move we tend to move our muscles in specific patterns or sequences. These sequences allow us to produce greater force and power by adding the force and power produced by the first set of muscles to that produced by the second, and so on. A classic example would be throwing a ball. The movement begins with a pushing and pivoting using the muscles of the leg (*gastrocnemius* and *soleus*). The muscles of the thigh (*quadriceps* and *abductors*) are then used to drive the body forward and pivot the hips. The core or *serape* muscles (see Figure 3-20) then pivot the shoulders around the hips to add even greater force and acceleration. Finally the rotator cuff muscles (*anterior deltoids* and *pectoralis major*) ac-

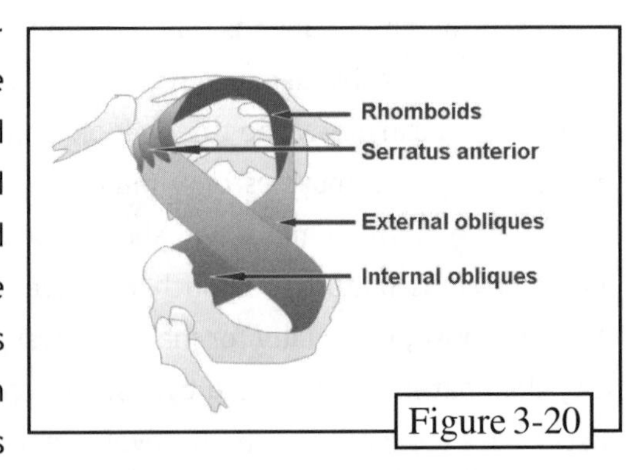

Figure 3-20

Example of Movement Specificity

Figure 3-21

celerate the shoulder forward, and the elbow extensors (*triceps surae*) and wrist flexors (*flexor carpi radialis* and *flexor carpi ulnaris*) then complete the movement adding the final increment of force and acceleration (see Figure 3-21). Most coaches, trainers, and exercise scientists believe that to maximize performance at least some component of the training must use multi-joint, sequential movements that simulate the task being trained. Unfortunately the concept of movement specificity is often overlooked even by practitioners of so-called "functional" training programs.

Motor Pattern Specificity

As we noted in Chapter 2, training can modify the brain and the nervous system so that they become better at performing a movement. Studies have shown that the motor map of the brain (*homunculus*, see Chapter 2, Figure 2-2) can actually be modified with training so that the nerves favoring the motion being trained occupy a greater area of the motor cortex. We feel this "re-mapping" of the brain as we practice skills. For example, remember when you first learned to ride a bike. You tried to pay attention to everything, moving the handlebars to maintain balance and change direction, keeping your body balanced correctly on the seat, keeping your feet on the pedals, or applying the correct force to the breaks so you didn't go over the handlebars. You were literally "all over the place" and most of the time that "all over the place" was "all over the ground". Then as you practiced, you got a "feel" for the skill. Pretty soon a lot of the things you had to pay careful attention to before became natural or "hardwired". This allowed you to concentrate on the more refined components of riding like keeping from hitting a stone in the road or negotiating a sharp turn that would have been disastrous in your earlier learning days. In addition to the restructuring of the brain, the nerves that go to specific muscles can also be changed (as described in Chapter 2) to make movements more efficient.

The take-home message of this whole "re-mapping" concept is that training done to enhance performance in sports or everyday activities should simulate to the greatest extent possible, the motor pattern of that activity. We will explore this concept in more practical terms in Chapter 9.

Joint Angle Specificity

In addition to targeting specific muscles, weight training can also affect the range of motion through which a joint can move and even the angle at which it produces its greatest strength. This is very important for a number of reasons. First, when a muscle is not worked through its full range of motion its overall length can shorten. Any of you who have been in a cast, or know someone who has, know that when the cast is removed the limb often takes months to regain full range of motion. This is because the muscle has adapted by shortening its length to the length at which it was immobilized. Another obvious example is the tight hamstring muscles seen in distance runners who don't stretch. Since the range of motion of the knees during distance running is limited, the muscle adapts to this shorter length and the joint loses flexibility if not stretched on a regular basis. The good news is that performing weight training exercise through the full range of motion can actually increase your flexibility and the range of motion of your joints. This may also be a good place to dispel the common myth that weight training will make you *muscle-bound*. While the physical size of a muscle may limit the range of motion of a joint to a small degree, most studies confirm that weight training increases rather than decreases flexibility when done through the full range of motion of the joint.

Example of small hip angle.

Figure 3-22A

The second important aspect of joint angle specificity has to do with training for specific sports or activities. It has been demonstrated that the greatest strength and power gains for any joint are at the angle at which it is worked. Therefore, in order to obtain strength through the entire range of motion of a joint, the full range must be worked. There are exercise machines designed to maximize resistance through the full range of motion of a joint. These will be examined in Chapter 5, but let's further consider the athlete who wishes to maximize performance in a specific sport. Research has shown that different athletes develop their greatest levels of strength and power at different joint angles. For example, cyclists have been shown to develop their greatest power at small hip angles (i.e. the angle of the hip to the leg), while runners produce theirs at large hip angles. This is because cycling and running work the muscles at smaller and larger hip angles, respectively (see Figure 3-22A & B). This concept, called *joint angle specificity,* indicates that to maximize performance in specific sports and activities it is not only important to consider the muscles and joints

Example of large hip angle.

Figure 3-22B

being used in that activity, but also the joint angles through which the activity is being performed. Considering these factors allows the training program to become even more effective.

Speed Specificity

Perhaps the most recognized example of specificity of training as it applies to the biomechanics of lifting is *speed specificity*. This concept states that the greatest gains in strength will occur at or slightly below the speed at which the training occurs. While some scientific studies have disagreed with this concept, the majority of the studies support it to some degree. To understand the importance of speed specificity it is first important to understand the distinction between two terms we have used in this text, strength and power. Simply defined, strength is a measure of the maximum amount of force which a muscle can produce. Therefore, the stronger an individual is the more weight he or she can move.

Power is quite different. Power is the *rate* (speed) at which force can be produced. It is the product of the force and the velocity of movement.

Power = Force x Velocity

Therefore, there are two factors that control the amount of power our muscles can produce: how strong we are and how quickly we can move. There is a curve that can be applied to resistance training called a load-velocity curve, and while it varies from joint to joint and muscle to muscle, it's general shape is rather consistent (see Figure 3-23). Figure 3-23 shows something that is very obvious to all of us. As the load (shown on the vertical or y- axis) goes up the speed or velocity of the movement (shown on the horizontal or x-axis) goes down. You can test this yourself using a simple lift like the arm curl. The less weight you put on the bar, the faster you can move it. The heavier the bar is, the more it resists your movement and the slower you will move. If the bar is loaded to the maximum you can hold, you can't move it at all, and if it is loaded with more weight than you can hold, it actually pulls your arm down when you wish to raise it. In

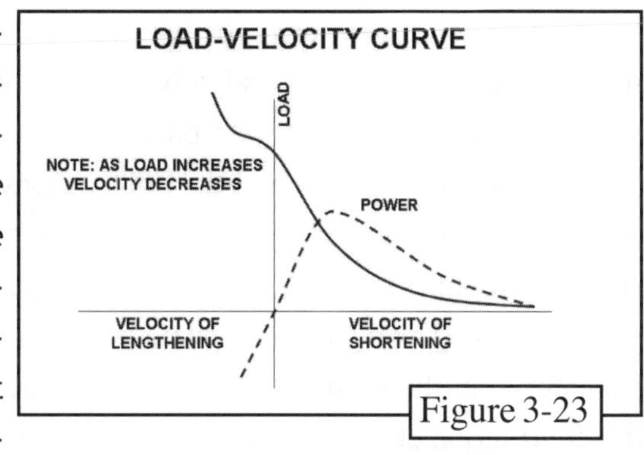

Figure 3-23

physics *speed* is a measure of how fast an object is moving *regardless of direction*, while *velocity* is a measure of how fast it is moving *in a specific direction*. Since a weight pulling your arm downward is actually in the opposite direction of the intended movement of a lift, it is termed negative velocity because the weight is pulling your arm at a certain speed in a direction you don't wish to go. Lifters often use this technique to develop strength and mass, and it is named after this negative velocity and thus called a *negative*.

Since power is the product of both strength and velocity, many researchers and strength coaches believe that power increases are best achieved by lowering the amount of weight being lifted and increasing the movement speed. Others believe that high loads and slow speeds should be the only methods used in the weight room and that speed is best addressed using drills performed outside the weight room. It is not the intent of this book to present a definitive answer to this debate; however, in our chapter on weight training prescription we will present both sides of the debate and offer a compromise that seems feasible.

The Stretch-Shortening Cycle

The connective tissues that support the muscles and connect them to the bones, and the proteins that make up the muscle cell's support system (often called a *cyto- skeleton, cyto=cell*) have a good amount of elasticity. This elasticity causes these tissues to "spring back" like an elastic band when they are stretched. As noted in Chapter 2 this rebound effect is called the *stretch-shortening cycle*. We use the stretch-shortening cycle every time we move. It is especially evident when we attempt to make powerful or explosive movements. For example, if you try to jump you will notice that no matter how you stand, legs straight, knees slightly bent, or knees bent at a deep angle, you always stoop down a bit further before you jump. This is a classic maneuver. Lowering the body quickly creates a high-speed eccentric contraction of the quadriceps. We end this contraction by abruptly stopping our body. These two actions cause the connective tissues to stretch and store mechanical energy. The mechanical energy stored in the elastic tissue is then released during the concentric contraction of the jump. This means that the elastic rebound of the connective tissues is added to the powerful contraction of the muscles to give even more power and greater height (see Figure 3-24). Although the *stretch-shortening cycle* is trained during most weight training exercises since connective tissue strength is increased, the most effective method of training the cycle is through *plyometric* training.

Jumping is an example of the stretch-shortening cycle.

Figure 3-24

Chapters 2 and 3 have presented the bases for the training technique that will be presented in the remainder of the book. As we explain the links between the science and application, you will develop the ability to design and modify lifting programs to meet specific needs and goals.

Chapter

4

The Language of Lifting

Weight lifting, like any other discipline, has its own language. The vocabulary allows coaches, trainers, and other exercise professionals, as well as those examining training theory, to efficiently convey information about training programs. To help you navigate your way around a gym and to prevent you from looking, feeling, and sounding out of place, it is important to understand this "gym lingo"!

The Basics

The basic unit of measurement in the weight room is the *repetition*, which is commonly called the *rep*. It refers to a complete movement including both the concentric and eccentric portion of a lift. Reps are grouped together to form a *set*. A set can be defined as a group of reps strung together with limited hesitation between them. If you are performing multiple sets, your muscles need a chance to recover, so a prescribed time is usually allotted for adequate rest between sets. This time is dictated by the purpose of the training session, your fitness level, and the intensity of the exercise. The amount of weight used or *load* is also referred to as the *resistance*. It is one measure of intensity during weight training. Therefore, intensity is commonly used to describe the amount of resistance used per set. It can also be used to indicate increases in the velocity of a movement or its difficulty level due to biomechanical efficiency (see Chapter 3). When choosing the weight that will be used for each set, we often select a weight that represents a percentage of our *Maximum* or *Max*. The maximum weight that can be lifted for one repetition (100% effort) is called the *Repetition Maximum* or *RM* for short. Occasionally, you will see the term written as 1RM, 3RM, 5RM or higher. The number in front of the RM refers to the maximum number of reps that you can achieve at a specific weight. For example, if you can lift 100 pounds for one all-out attempt, then 100 pounds is your 1RM. At a lower weight, say 90 pounds, you may be able to get 3 reps for a 3RM of 90 pounds.

Proper Exercise Notation:

3 x 8 x 100 or
3 x 8 x 80% or
3 x 8RM

Meaning 3 sets of 8 reps at 100 pounds or 80% of 1RM or at an 8RM load.

Forms of Resistance

There are several forms of resistance, each providing a slightly different way of loading the muscles. The two most common forms of resistance are free-weights and stack-weights. The term *free-weights* has nothing to do with how much they cost. Rather the term means that the weights are loose and can be added to a barbell, dumbbell, machine, or just held in your hand. *Plate* is the nickname for a free weight. *Stack-weight* is the type of weight used on machines. These weights commonly travel along rods and require a "pin" to select and hold the desired load. For this reason, stack-weight machines are often called *selectorized machines*. Other possibilities include: pneumatic (air driven) machines, hydraulic or fluid driven machines, rubber bands or tubes, and rods (see Figure 4-1). We will present each of these options and their strengths and weaknesses in Chapter 5.

PRINCIPLES OF EXERCISE

In Chapter 8 you will learn how to put exercise programs together based on what you want to accomplish. In general, however, there

Various Forms of Resistance

Figure 4-1

are several underlying principles that are the basis for training. Getting a solid base by understanding the essential components will help you get the most bang for your exercise buck.

Warm-Up and Cool-Down

Before starting or finishing any workout, a proper *warm-up* and *cool-down* should be employed. *Warm-ups* prepare the body physiologically for exercise by increasing body temperature, facilitating proper blood flow, and increasing soft-tissue pliability and overall flexibility. A *cool-down* is extremely important because it allows the body to gradually reduce its temperature. It also allows the blood to be redistributed from the working muscles to the other organs, thereby reducing the probability of dizziness and light-headedness that can follow exercise.

Workout

Contrary to popular opinion, just showing up at the gym and talking about training does not constitute a workout. You must exercise for a period of time to effectively promote change. A *workout* is simply performing exercise during your training session or *training*.

Consistency

For true adaptation to take place, you need to string a number of workout days together. They don't have to be back to back; however, working out once a month will not promote adaptation. Selecting a specific period of time for exercise each day helps make your workout a part of your regular routine and provides a *consistent* pattern of training.

The Frequency, Intensity, Time (FIT) Principle

There are a number of basic variables that can be manipulated during exercise programming. FIT is an acronym that includes three of them. As with many acronyms the concepts are a bit jumbled and incomplete; but we will use FIT as a cueing system for the training variables. *Frequency* refers to the number of times per week you work out. *Intensity* is the resistance and speed at which you perform the exercise. *Time* can refer to the amount of rest between sets and/or the length of time (*duration*) a particular set takes to complete. To these variables we should also add one more critical variable, *volume*, which is the number of sets multiplied by the number of reps and can also use load as part of the equation. Of course, it's very difficult to pronounce FITV.

Specificity and the SAID Principle

SAID is another training acronym, but this one works a bit better than FIT. To realize maximum gains in your physiological systems, activities and programs should be selected with a specific goal in mind. The *Specific Adaptation to Imposed Demand* (SAID) principle states that when the body is subjected to a specific overload, it will gradually adapt to deal with that overload. In short, the muscle will re-engineer itself to meet the needs imposed on it. You probably remember the theories of specificity presented in Chapters 2 and 3. The SAID principle represents the practical application of these concepts.

Overload Principle

The overload principle states that for a component of fitness to improve, the related system must work harder than it is normally accustomed to working (see Figure 4-2). For weight training, *overload* may be established in a variety of ways including: changing the load; manipulating the sets, reps, and rest; modifying the speed of the movement; or changing the exercises used. As you will see in Chapter 9, this principle is one of the components of successful periodization cycling.

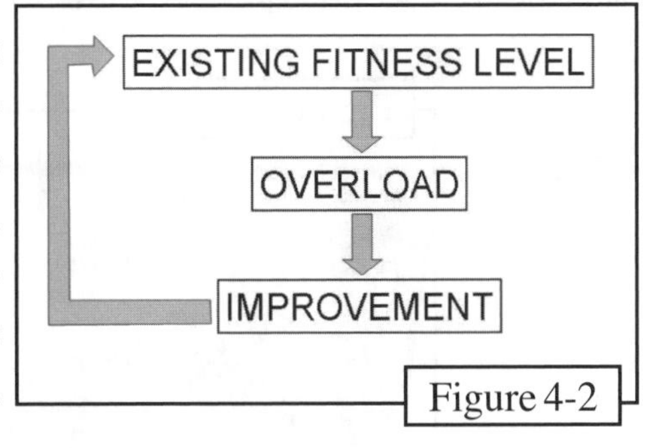

Figure 4-2

Individuality

Each person responds to exercise differently and has his or her unique genetic potential and existing level of fitness (Figure 4-3). Therefore, exercise programs should be specifically designed for the individual. Add to this the fact that people may have very different fitness goals, physical abilities, and levels of motivation, and the case for *individuality* becomes even stronger. It is important to recognize these concepts because your workout partner, friend, or client may respond quite differently than you to the same exercise stimulus. A common analogy that I like to use is called "tasting the sauce". When a good cook is making spaghetti sauce, "he" has a general recipe telling him what ingredients go into the sauce and approximately how much of each. But as the sauce is cooking he goes back and tastes it, adding a bit of this and a pinch of that until he has the sauce tasting exactly the way he likes it. He has to do this because the ingredients; the fresh tomatoes, basil, parsley, and other items, will all be a bit different each time he purchases them, and he doesn't know exactly how they will respond during the cooking process.

If the cook can't predict how things as genetically uncomplicated as tomatoes, parsley, and basil will react to a simple cooking process, how can we expect different human beings to react the same to a lifting stimulus. The simple answer is, we can't. And that is why this principle of individuality will be used so extensively in the evolving diagnostic/prescription model that we will present later in this book.

Figure 4-3

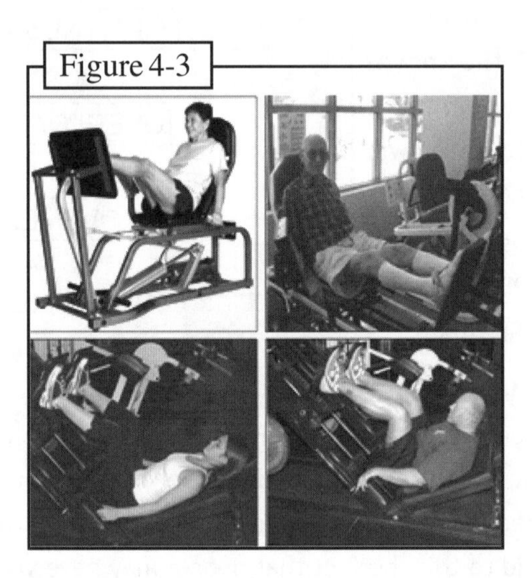

Progression

A common training error is the adaptation of the "no pain, no gain" adage. However, pain is not the measure of a good workout and is often an indicator of injury. Therefore, pain should be avoided altogether if possible. Exercising is very much like building a house, you must start with a solid foundation if you are to achieve your goals and prevent injury. Start gradually and make small changes during successive workouts. This is called a logical *progression*. To accomplish this you may gradually increase the number of sets or reps, use more resistance or higher speeds, reduce rest, or vary your training techniques.

This theory not only governs the rate at which you apply increases in intensity, volume, and frequency, it is also the factor that dictates the lengths of the specific training cycle, how those cycles evolve in the training process, and the reason why we suggest tissue adaptation cycles when an individual is starting a training program, starting a new or different training cycle, or returning to training after a prolonged layoff period.

Exercise Tolerance

Each muscle of the body will have a certain level of exercise that it can tolerate without excessive damage or fatigue. As an individual trains, the level of exercise *tolerance* will be increased as the muscle restructures itself. Failure to respect the concept of exercise tolerance may lead to soreness, injury, and in the worst case scenario, the necessity to stop training all together and visit your local sports medicine clinic. The fact that a muscle and its connective tissue will change and be better able to handle higher levels of exercises is the basis of progression, periodization, and the success of Tissue Adaptation Cycles.

TRAINING TERMINOLOGY

In addition to the basic terms used to convey information on training intensity, volume, and response, there are other terms are used to describe the training methods employed in the weight room. Many have scientific and practical relevance; however, most are part of the "gym lingo" developed by the people doing the actual lifting.

Pre-Exhaust or Post-Exhaust System

A *pre-exhaust system* is when a muscle (or group of muscles) is exercised using a set of one exercise (the pre-exhaustion exercise) followed immediately by a set of a different exercise. In this system minimal recovery time is allowed between sets. The pre-exhaustion exercise is usually a single-joint exercise targeting a larger muscle group, and the subsequent exercise is usually a double or multi-joint movement involving that same

> Single Joint Exercises are isolation exercises involving only 1 joint or 1 particular muscle group. A Multi Joint Exercise involves two or more groups of muscles and joints.

muscle group and its synergists. The purpose is to fatigue the larger muscle group prior to performing another exercise that involves that muscle and its synergists (helpers). For example, the bench press exercise may be preceded by an isolated pec fly movement (see Figure 4-4). In this example, the pectorals and anterior deltoids may fatigue during the flys, but the triceps can help these muscles during the bench press allowing more fibers in the pecs to be recruited during the second (bench press) set.

Isolated Pec Fly Movement — Bench Press Exercise

Figure 4-4

The *post-exhaust system* is similar to the pre-exhaust system except that the "exhaustive" movement follows the initial movement. Generally, a post-exhaust exercise is a single-joint movement that isolates a particular muscle group. This movement will follow a multi-joint where the muscle is partially fatigued as it works in conjunction with its synergists.

There are three central ideas behind these two methods of training. The first is that performing an exhaust system exercise immediately before or after a major movement can provide a greater level of overload for the targeted muscle group. This is especially true when a smaller stabilizer muscle has the potential to limit the level stimulus to the targeted muscle group (as in the bench press example) where the anterior deltoids may be helping to move the load to a greater degree with each repetition. The second idea is that an exhaust system exercise increases the ability to isolate a muscle or muscle group that is "hard" to target. This is accomplished by partially fatiguing the targeted muscle group using a single joint movement and then using the synergists during a multi-joint movement to "help" the muscle to do even more work (pre-exhaustion) or fatiguing the synergists (multi-joint movement) before the muscle group is targeted using a single joint isolation movement (post-exhaustion). The third idea is that the exhaust system exercises can be used to increase conditioning because they extend the length of a "normal" set by 30 seconds or more. This also makes exhaust systems viable methods for training muscles to "tolerate" lactic acid.

Drop/Strip/Burn Sets

The term drop (or strip) is used to describe the act of decreasing the resistance during a set. *Drop* sets, often referred to as burn sets, are designed to extend the length of a set by gradually decreasing the intensity. The drop is accomplished by reducing the resistance by either removing plates (free-weight exercises) or by moving the pin to a lower weight (machine exercises) (Figure 4-5). Simply stated, the lifter completes a prescribed number of reps to a point of failure, then the weight is immediately decreased and more reps are performed. At the point of failure after the first drop, the lifter can either continue with another drop or end the set.

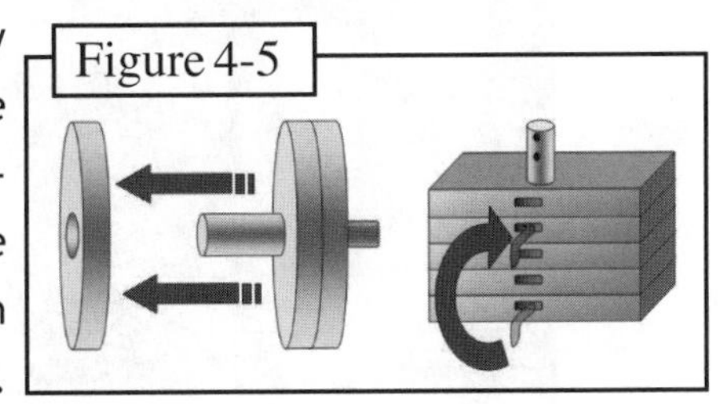
Figure 4-5

The number of drops will vary depending on the goal of the exercise and the ability of the lifter. A *burn* set is a type of drop set. It is often called a partial since the strategy that allows you to perform extra reps is to use only the last five or six inches of a rep as opposed to dropping or decreasing the weight, as would be the case in a classic drop set.

Negatives

A *negative* is an exercise designed to emphasize the eccentric portion of a lift (recall Chapter 3 and the discussion of the load-velocity curve). Since we can lower much more weight than we can lift, the idea behind this type of training is to use the eccentric movement to load the muscle beyond the resistance possible during either a concentric or full (concentric/eccentric) movement. The disadvantage of this technique is that it can be dangerous and requires a spotter to help reset the weight during the concentric movement (Figure 4-6). The lifter can use free-weights, machines, or even manual pressure to produce the negative load. The exercise can be performed in a variety of ways, but the overall goal is to use a greater load during the eccentric portion of the lift. Negative reps should take at least 5 seconds to perform and should only be done by experienced lifters with proper spotting. Due to the

> A *spotter* is a training partner that assists with a lift when the lifter becomes fatigued.

Negative exercises require a spotter.

Figure 4-6

eccentric nature of these lifts they often result in a high level of DOMS. This method is not for the beginning lifter.

DOMS is short for Delayed Onset Muscle Soreness which is usually felt a day or two after exercise.

Forced Repetitions – Exhaust

Although performing extra reps during an exercise can increase the degree of overload, it is difficult and even dangerous without the help of an experienced spotter. *Forced reps*, as the name implies, means having someone help with the final few reps, thereby allowing the lifter to continue with a set which he or she could not complete alone (see Figure 4-7). When performing a forced rep it is very important that the spotter provides only enough help to continue the bar moving and does not lift the weight for the lifter. The spotter should be strong enough to lift the weight and skilled at this method of training or this type of training should not be attempted. As was the case for negative training, this method is recommended for advanced lifters only.

When performing forced repetitions, a spotter is used to help complete the final few reps.

Figure 4-7

Superset/Multi-Set

When time is of the essence, the *superset* works well. It allows a lifter to perform two (super) or more (multi-) exercises one after the other with little or no rest between exercises. The lifter completes the first set of the first exercise and without rest, moves to the next exercise. The next exercise is usually an exercise that works the opposite or antagonist muscle group. For example, the lifter would perform a set of leg extensions immediately followed by a set of leg curls with no rest between sets (see Figures 4-8). A second alternative is to perform a second set that uses the same muscle group but

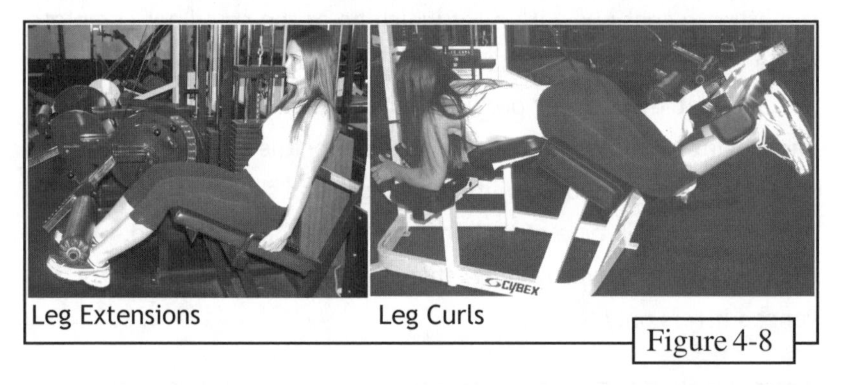

Leg Extensions Leg Curls

Figure 4-8

relies more heavily on different synergists, such as following a set of lat pull downs with a set of straight arm pull downs. The *multi-set* system may combine 3 or more exercises such as a triceps pushdown, biceps curl, and shoulder lateral raise. The longer the exercise continues without rest, the greater the likelihood that fatigue will occur, even when working different muscles. This system is very effective, but you should have a goal in mind before you begin. A group of multi-sets strung together form a "circuit". A *circuit* is a training program that involves performing several exercises in a row with little or no rest between exercises. This is another effective way of training multiple muscle groups in a single workout. Circuits are also used to maintain high metabolic levels, and in some special cases, they can even produce significant increases in cardiovascular fitness.

Giant Sets

This is also called "rest-pause" training. A *giant set* involves performing a series of near maximal reps with very short rests between them, followed by a longer rest which completes the giant set. The lifter uses a resistance that is near maximal for about a 2-3RM (see Figure 4-9). Between each "max" the lifter rests about 10-15 seconds. Then another rep is performed with the same weight followed by another 10-15 second rest. When the lifter can no longer make the lift (usually after about 5-7 reps), a much longer (5min) rest is given, completing the giant set. While in theory this seems plausible for developing strength, the main drawbacks are that it is time consuming and the weight calculation (for the reps) must be precise to maximize gain and reduce the potential for injury.

A 10-15 second rest is taken between each near maximal rep when perfoming a giant set.

Figure 4-9

Pyramid System

Just as the name *pyramid system* implies, the lifter pyramids the weight and/or reps. In other words, as each set progresses, either the weight, the reps, or both are increased or decreased according to the specific protocol. There are three versions with three kinds of pyramids, producing nine different pyramid schemes. The major drawback with a pyramid is that the lifter has to "save" strength for later sets. This type of exercise system dedicates a lot of time to a single exercise and the literature supporting the benefits of pyramid training is sparse. The following table shows the possible scenarios that can be used during pyramid training.

Pyramid Up	Increase Weight / Decrease Reps	Increase Reps / Decrease Weight	Increase Both
Pyramid Down	Decrease Weight / Increase Reps	Decrease Reps / Increase Weight	Decrease Both
Pyramid Up & Pyramid Down	Increase Weight / Decrease Reps Up - Reverse the System Down	Increase Reps / Decrease Weight Up -Reverse the System Down	Increase Both Up Decrease Both Down

Concentration or Blitz System

The *concentration* or *blitz* system concentrates on a specific muscle, muscle group, or movement. The entire workout is spent on this body part or movement. For bodybuilders this type of routine can help concentrate workouts on weaker or smaller body parts (such as biceps or calves). However, for most body parts this level of concentration is not going to provide an optimal training benefit and may produce a high level of DOMS. This system is one way to add variety to a program, especially after the main goal has been met. In general, blitz training requires several sessions per week to train the entire body and is usually not practical for most people.

Split Training

Split training is a common training technique that requires the body to be divided into a number of areas, each of which is targeted on a specified day or days. A split may use a simple pattern such as targeting the upper body one day and lower the next. It may also use more complex patterns where areas of the upper and lower body are also "split" into separate training days. Working the chest, triceps, and shoulders one day and back and biceps another day is an example of a split. Split training is very effective if your goal is bodybuilding, and you can visit the weight room many times during the week. Another variation of the split involves splitting the workout on the same day, such as training lower body parts in the morning and upper body parts in the evening.

Push/Pull

Push/pull training is a marriage of the split training system and the superset system. It involves training push movements on one day and pull movements on the other day, or training both push/pull movements on the same day by alternating exercises. The pattern of alternating exercises may use a superset or may incorporate a rest between sets. A modification of this system is to perform all the sets of a specific push or pull exercise before moving on to the opposing exercise. For example, an athlete may do three sets of bench press followed by three sets of seated row (see Figure 4-10). This method is good if time is an issue, and the goal is muscular balance. We often spend too much time working the muscles we see and forget about their antagonists. This "mirror consciousness" (see Figure 4-11) often leads to chronic or acute injury due to muscle imbalances. The push/pull system eliminates this problem.

Push/pull training involves training push movements separately from pull movements.

Figure 4-10

Figure 4-11

Bulking and Flushing

Bulking and *flushing* are two methods of training that are most commonly used by bodybuilders. The purpose of these methods is to increase the overall size of the muscle. Bulking is much like concentration or blitzing the muscle and is a gym term for hitting a particular body part extra hard. Flushing refers to increasing the blood flow to the muscle to improve the overall size. While this might seem important in theory, it really only leads to temporary increases in size due to the engorging of the muscle with blood.

> Flushing is also used to describe the removal of lactic acid via lifting weights. However, this is a bit of a contradiction in terms since overall lactic acid levels are probably increasing during the act of lifting, and washout is only occurring when tension is released by the muscle at the end of a rep set.

Shocking

Considering that every time you lift weights you tend to "shock" the muscles used, the term *shocking* has lost much of its intended meaning over the years. In gym lingo, it refers to forcing your muscles to undergo a "more than they are used to" stimulus. The term shocking has now been almost completely replaced by the term overload. However, a true shock treatment would be performing an exercise employing a larger than normal overload.

21's

This is a hugely popular technique with very little evidence to support it as a viable training method for anything other than variety. *21's* involve doing two series of seven-limited range of motion reps, followed by seven full range of motion reps. The most common exercise employing 21's is the arm curl. Using this exercise, the lifter would do seven reps moving from a fully extended position to the halfway point (forearms straight out from the body) (4-12A), then immediately perform seven reps from the halfway point to the fully flexed position (4-12B), and immediately perform seven full range arm curls (4-12C). This is difficult and has the potential to cause a good deal of microscopic muscle damage (DOMS). Therefore, we suggest that it be considered an advanced technique and not be employed by beginning lifters.

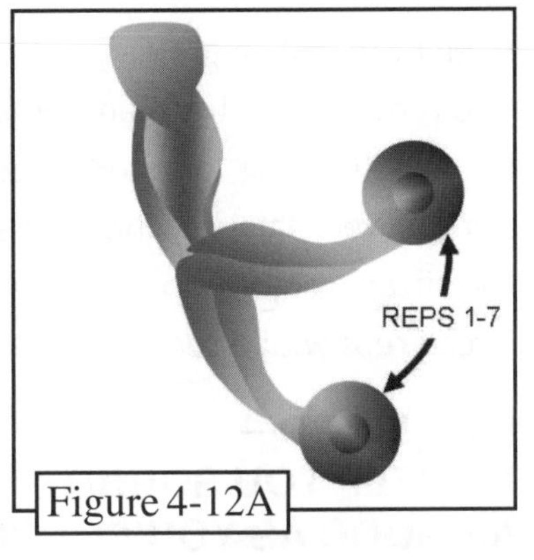

Figure 4-12A

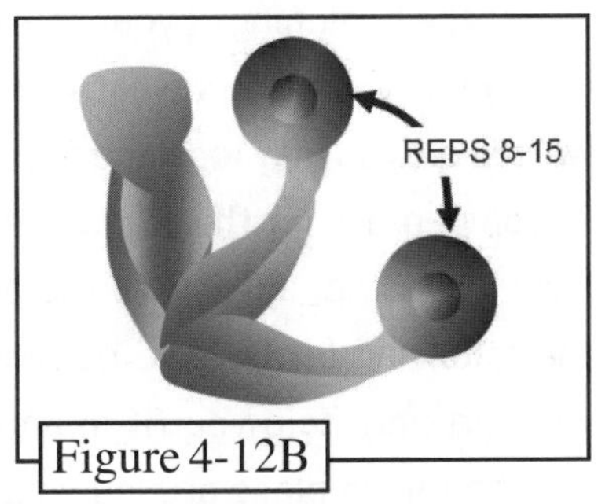

Figure 4-12B

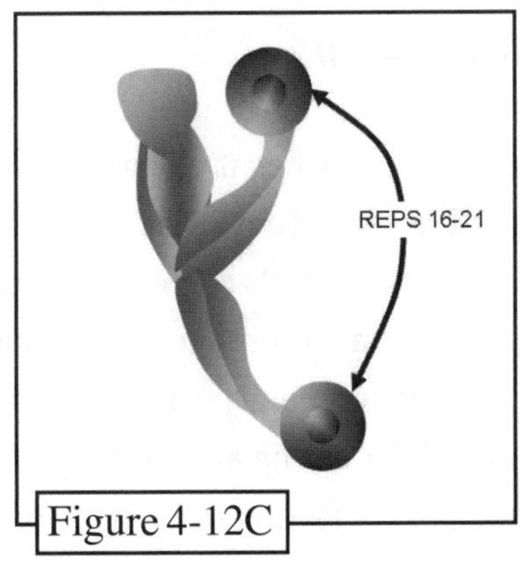

Figure 4-12C

Cheat Reps

A *cheat rep* or *cheating* is the act of performing a rep or reps using accessory muscles to move the weight. It usually involves "swinging the weight" in hopes of achieving a complete repetition (see Figure 4-13). To perform a cheat rep, the lifter must break form and incorporate "helper" muscles to complete the movement. Other than an attempt to look impressive in the gym, cheat reps provide very little additional benefit to the muscle being targeted since the load is being moved mainly by the accessory muscles. The lifter would accomplish more by doing forced reps with a spotter.

Example of a cheat rep.

Figure 4-13

GYM LINGO – TO HELP YOU SOUND AS GOOD AS YOU'LL LOOK

At the beginning of your training, you may not look like you know what you are doing, or worse yet, you may look and feel out of place. To compensate for this it may help to "speak the lingo" so you sound knowledgeable, at least to the other gym "regulars". While most of the following terms have no real scientific meaning, knowing them will certainly help you fit in and understand the conversations that may be taking place around you.

The Pump

This is a term used to describe the full feeling that a muscle experiences when it is engorged with blood and feels like it has reached its "bursting" point. The pump is accomplished by keeping the muscle under tension throughout a set. This creates pressure within the muscle that traps (occludes) a large volume of the circulating blood, thereby, temporarily increasing the size of the muscle. Occasionally, especially during arm curls, you will also hear the term "squeeze at the top" referring to flexing completely to enhance the pump.

Cutting Up

Often called getting ripped or shredded, this term does not refer to how you chop your veggies. In the world of super-lean, well-built people it refers to the chiseled, often sculpted look that some people attain by combining a calorie-restricted diet with a high-energy work-out program (Figure 4-14).

The V and the Six-Pack

A shredded or ripped person.
Figure 4-14

The V is the shape that the lats make when they taper down toward the waist (provided the waist doesn't bulge) (Figure 4-15). The six-pack is what the abdominal region looks like when a person is "shredded". In actual fact, there are eight abdominal sections formed by tendinous connections within the muscles. Having a six-pack is also referred to as having "cubes in the tray" since well-defined abdominals resemble an ice cube tray (Figure 4-16). A third term used to describe a well-defined abdominal section is the "washboard". This refers to the late 1920's style clothes washing device. The number of nicknames given to the abdominals is a testament to the attention they get in the gym environment. Having a good six-pack is one of the most enviable qualities among regular exercisers.

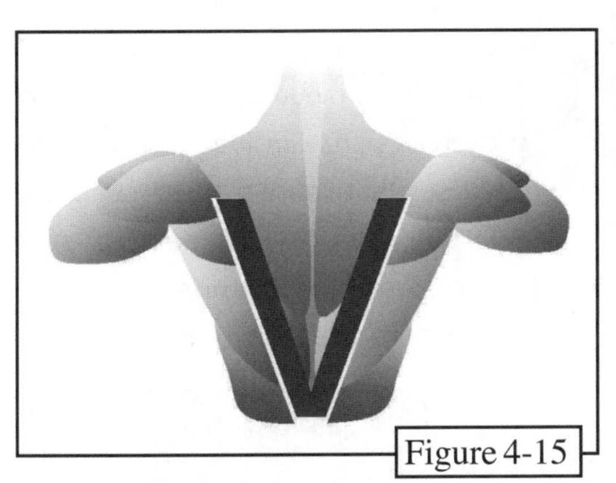

Figure 4-15

Striated

Striated is yet another in the long line of terms used to describe being ripped. The term describes a muscle that is so lean that it shows separations between fibers. In fact, the term comes from the striped appearance that skeletal muscles show under a microscope due to their repeating sarcomere structure (see Chapter 2). However, the lines seen in these well-cut or striated muscles actually run perpendicular to the striations in a muscle fiber. As noted above, they are actually formed by the connective tissue between fiber bundles.

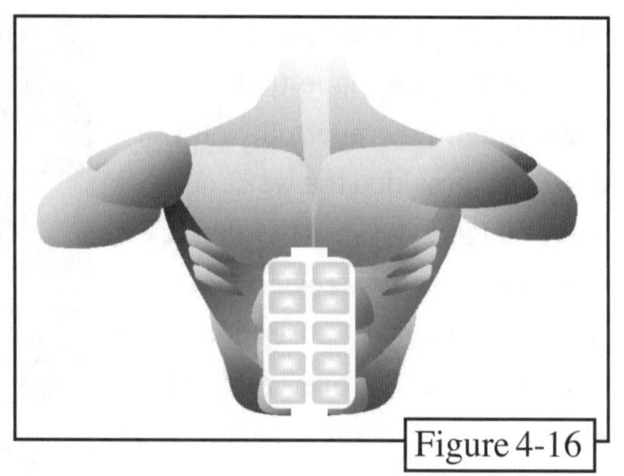

Figure 4-16

Mass and Peak

These are two terms used to describe the size and shape of a muscle. *Mass* refers to the size or volume of a muscle. *Peak* refers to a muscle's shape (Figure 4-17). If a muscle has a great peak it has an abrupt increase in size from the tendon to the belly of a muscle making it look like a mountain peak. Peaking exercises are considered special exercises that cause a muscle to bulge in this way. Most of these are supported by "gym knowledge" rather than hard scientific evidence.

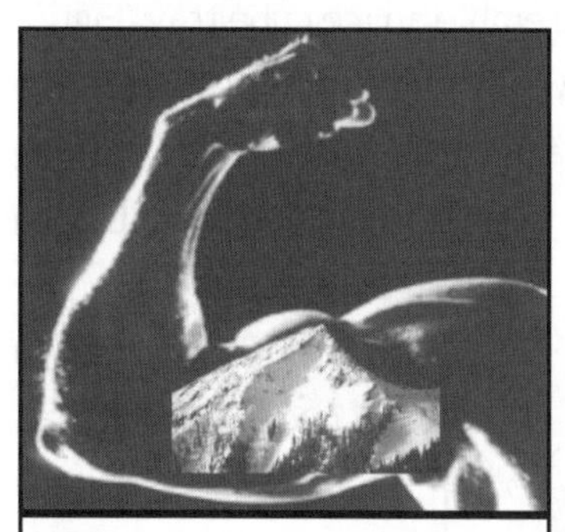

Peak refers to a muscles shape.

Figure 4-17

Being Vascular

Being vascular is a term used to describe the appearance of a lifter. It refers to an individual whose muscles have large, visible veins which become especially prominent after "getting a pump" (Figure 4-18).

A vascular person's muscles have large, visible veins.

Figure 4-18

Being Dialed In

Dialed in means having a perfectly designed program that attends specifically to the goals of the lifter. Obviously, since different individuals will have different goals there is no single program or workout that is best for "dialing in". We will be presenting methods for dialing in to specific goals in Chapter 9.

Maxing Out or Going For a PR

Maxing out means to attempt a 1RM during that workout day. The PR stands for Personal Record and is sometimes called a PB for Personal Best. This practice, while being a real ego booster, is very dangerous and serves little purpose except during organized competitions or scientific studies.

Guns and Wheels

Guns refer to the arms. When large they are called bazookas (Figure 4-19). When they are small, they are called pistols. Wheels, or pins if they are thin, refer to the legs. If you are the biggest person in the gym then you can call body parts anything you like such as wings, pipes, or posts.

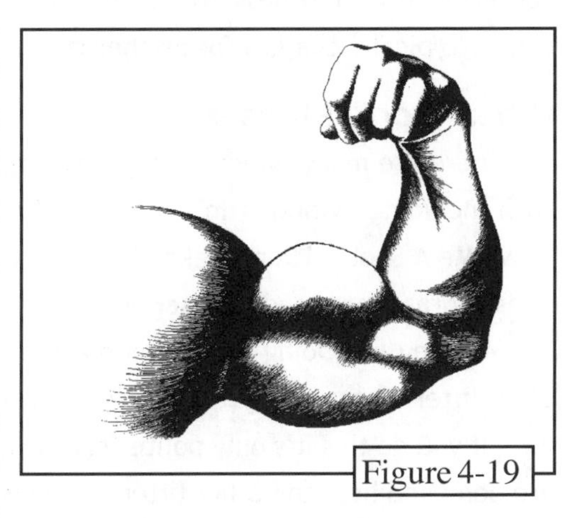

Figure 4-19

The Sticking Point

The sticking point is a point in the range of motion of the lift where the weight gets stuck! In biomechanical terms, it is the point where the body is at a mechanical disadvantage, thus decreasing the force output of the musculoskeletal unit and causing the bar to slow down or even stop during the lift. You will recall from Chapters 2 and 3 that the muscle has a length where it produces the greatest force and each joint has an angle where it is at its greatest mechanical advantage. Most lifters become familiar with their sticking points for specific exercises like the bench press or squat.

The Lockout

The lockout is the end portion of a lift. This is the final few inches of the movement and it tends to be difficult since the bar is traveling very slowly. In short, the lockout completes the lift.

'Roids and The Juice

'Roids and Juice are also sometimes called "the sauce". These terms refer to illegal supplementation using anabolic steroids in conjunction with weight training. While 'roids can dramatically increase muscle mass, the negative health impacts that the use of anabolic steroids can have on an individual far outweigh the benefits.

Personal Training or One-On-One

This is the act of engaging a training partner or instructor to help you achieve your fitness goals. As with any service, the personal trainer typically charges for his/her time.

Other "Cool" Phrases

There are many typical gym phrases that you should be familiar with including "Working In", "It's All You", "Just One More Rep", "Give Me A Spot", "Don't Take The Weight" and "Take The Weight". These phrases are used to describe some aspect of spotting or lifting.

Working In: Doing a set on a machine or at a station while another lifter is recovering from his set. The usage: "Hi, mind if I work in?" If you do this it's only polite to wipe down the bench when you are done and help the other lifter reset his or her plates or pin.

Just one more rep: This one gets used at the end of a fatiguing set when the lifter is having a difficult time finishing the last repetition. The spotter will usually help the lifter through the last rep while saying this. But a word of caution, the spotter must provide sufficient help and there should be good communication between the spotter and the lifter. No one wants "one more rep" to become "one more trip to the sports medicine clinic".

Give me a spot: When someone is doing a lift (usually with free weights) and would like another person to "watch and guide" that lift for safety, form, and performance purposes this is what they would say. Since each lift has its own spotting technique, be sure you know what you are doing before you consent to "spot".

Don't take the weight/Take the weight: This is pretty straight forward. When the lifter feels he can finish his final rep without assistance he will say to the spotter "don't take the weight". If he feels he can't complete the rep he will say "take the weight".

Don't be surprised when someone talks to you using this code, just smile, and do your best to either get out of their way (if it looks dangerous) or help out (if you have the ability). Just like the world of cyber space, the gym has a language of its own. In time you will become familiar with gym jargon and then you'll not only look the part, you'll be able to talk it too.

Chapter

5

Weight Training Equipment

Much like the advancement of other sports equipment, such as running shoes and tennis rackets, resistance training equipment has also evolved throughout the years. The American public's interest in fitness has created a competitive market where equipment manufacturers are continually designing new lifting equipment to meet the demand. While the old-fashioned dumbbell and barbell still make great training tools, they may not meet the diverse needs, expectations, and tastes of all individuals. Some of the new pieces of equipment on the market have the potential to bring variety to training routines and may also provide exercises that can target the needs of specific, unique populations.

The idea behind weight training equipment is quite simple - provide a form of resistance that challenges the particular muscle or muscles so that they will receive maximal stimulus in the most effective way. In addition, for optimal utilization the equipment should be capable of meeting the needs of many different populations. To design the most effective piece of equipment, however, is not easy. There are hundreds of equipment manufacturers offering many different machines, free-weight devices, and other types of equipment such as tubing, balls, and other implements which are designed to provide various forms of resistance. Selecting the appropriate equipment, and/or the gym that provides the kind of equipment you like, can be made easier if you know what equipment you want and why.

There are two basic classifications for exercise equipment: free-resistance (often called free-weights) and contained resistance (often called machine weights). Free-resistance is any device or plate weight that has no real moving parts and is completely controlled by the lifter. There is no predetermined resistance path and no specific settings that need to be established. In contrast, a contained resistance device has specific settings, and while the path of resistance may be quite variable, the resistance is still contained within the apparatus. In layman's terms, you can't drop the weight on your toes!

Besides the obvious cost issue, there are several factors that should be considered before purchasing a particular piece of equipment or joining a health club that uses a specific manufacturer's equipment line.

Safety

The issue of safety is paramount in any training program. Elite athletes possess greater skills and greater tolerance to exercise than the general public. Therefore, they may perform exercises that might be construed dangerous (and rightfully so) to the general population. The danger involved with most exercise equipment is not inherent in the equipment itself, but rather, related to how it is used. While it is true that most machines provide a safer environment because the apparatus is contained and the path of resistance is predetermined, free-weight exercises and the like can be just as safe when performed correctly. The issue then is one of exercise performance. In all cases, repetitions must be performed properly, and the body must be kept in the proper lifting position. Additionally, exercises where heavy loads are used or where the individual or body part is between the resistance and its path to the ground, spotters should be used to reduce the potential for injury (see Figure 5-1).

Spotters should be used to reduce potential for injury.

Figure 5-1

Adjustability

The more adjustable the piece of equipment, the greater the number of exercise variations it can accommodate and the more needs it can serve. Free-resistance devices, like free weights or tubes, favor adjustability since everyone and anyone can use them without needing to make adjustments for body size and type. It is extremely important to find equipment that fits your body type. If you are shorter than average or very tall, then fitting properly into certain machines may be difficult. If a machine has an adjustable seat and variable hand positions, it can accommodate a large cross-section of the exercising population (see Figure 5-2). These are also important to allow the critical alignment of the joint with the axis of rotation or the machine (Figure 5-3). Add to this the ability to adjust weights

Adjustable seats accommodate a large cross-section of the exercising population.

Figure 5-2

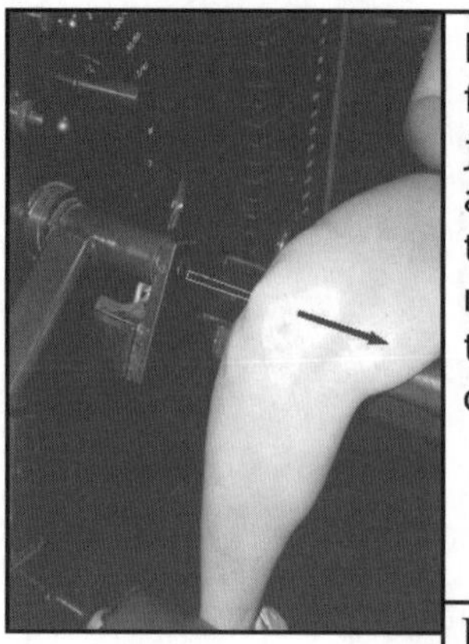

It is critical for the joint to align with the axis of rotation of the machine.

Figure 5-3

easily and in small increments across a large range of resistance and the adjustability of the machine is further enhanced (Figure 5-4). Remember, however, that adjustability is not the sole measure of the effectiveness of a machine. In many cases there is a trade-off. For example, a machine designed to target a specific muscle group does not have the capacity to train multiple muscles, but it does provide effective targeting with minimal practice or skill levels.

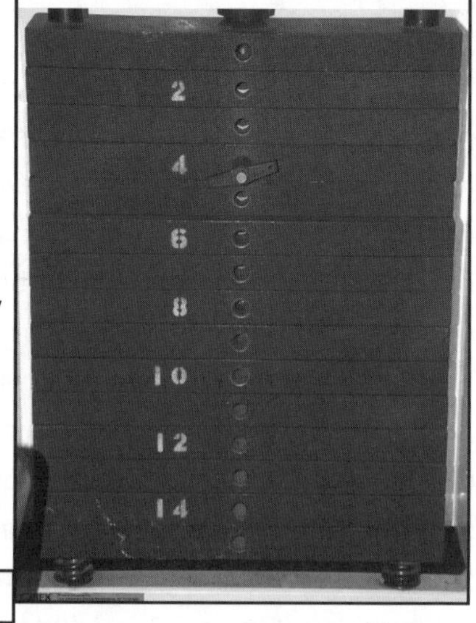

The ability to adjust weights easily and in small amounts enhances the adjustability of the machine.

Figure 5-4

Range of Motion

The general rule in weight training is to work a muscle through its full range of motion. A number of researchers have shown that muscles show their greatest levels of improvement within the range of motion at which they are trained. Therefore, a machine with a preset range of motion may limit the ability to design a training program that targets muscle in a specific way. These machines may also reduce the secondary benefits of weight training which include increases in flexibility and functional range of motion.

Additionally, certain machines dictate limb angles and body positions that do not allow people with injuries or functional limitations to utilize them comfortably. For example, a common problem is the inability of persons with low back disorders to use some lower body machines. Ideally, as long as the range of motion is pain-free, then that particular machine can be used. Be sure to try the machine to see if it fits your comfort zone before applying any load. Remember using a free-weight or a machine that incorporates a variable movement pattern (rather than a set pathway) improves the chances of finding a comfortable position in which to train. However, it also requires greater control of the resistance (Figure 5-5).

One final point, in some cases a shorter range of motion is appropriate. For example, an athlete might want to train a muscle to maximize performance using a movement pattern that is similar to that used in his or her sport. From the point of rehabilitation, a therapist might wish to incorporate limited range of motion exercises

Figure 5-5

As long as the range of motion is pain-free, then that particular machine can be used.

into the early stages of a training program to reduce the potential for injury to a muscle that has been shortened and atrophied due to limited use.

Isolation vs. Multi-Joint

Targeting a specific muscle certainly improves the capacity of an exercise to increase that muscle's size. However, in real-life activities, we seldom perform robotic, single joint movements. In today's training world it is becoming more commonplace to perform multi-joint movements that simulate everyday activities since these allow the targeting of unique needs and goals of specific populations. This does not mean that isolation movements are not good; however, due to limitations it may be necessary to perform multi-joint exercises to train more muscles. Isolation exercises are the preferred method to hypertrophy specific muscles or muscle groups (Figure 5-6A), while multi-joint movements are preferred when training is designed to improve performance in sports or everyday activities (Figure 5-6B). In our chapter on specific training prescriptions we will show how both can be incorporated at different stages of a training program.

Isolation exercises are the preferred method to hypertropy specific muscles. Figure 5-6A

Multi-joint movements are preferred when training to improve performance in sports or everyday activities. Figure 5-6B

Isolateral vs. Dual-Limb

Should you train one arm or both arms at once? The answer lies in the intention of the training program. When rehabilitation or muscular balance is an issue, isolateral or single limb movements are usually preferred. Dual limb devices may not be as effective in these situations since one limb may "take-over" if it is considerably stronger than the other (Figure 5-7A). In contrast, the dual limb machine tends to produce a better overall feel and reduces the amount of extraneous movement (Figure 5-7B). In addition, there is the time factor that was mentioned earlier. Working both limbs simultaneously takes half the time of training each limb separately. And finally, there may be the question of specificity. The dual limb movement may better match the motor pattern for which you are training.

If one limb is considerable stronger than the other it may "take over" when using a dual limb device.

Figure 5-7A

Dual limb machines produce a better overall feel, reduce extraneous movement, and take half the time of training limbs separately.

Figure 5-7B

Variable Movement Pathways

The newest resistance machines allow movements to be performed in several planes of motion. Rather than holding the movement to a specific line, with these machines there is no specific set pathway (only a set range within a pathway). They also provide the lifter with the best of both worlds since he or she must control the weight throughout the range of motion, while still being given the safety and guidance afforded by machine-based training (Figure 5-8). Proponents of these types of machines feel that since the lifter must exert considerable effort to stabilize the functioning joint, the muscle and its synergists are developed more completely. Opponents of these devices argue that the machines are almost free-weight like, so why not just use free-weights since they maximize both the use of synergist muscles and freedom of movement.

Resistance machines allow movements to be performed in several planes of motion.

Figure 5-8

Balance and Control

Machines nearly eliminate the need to maintain balance during the lift. Free-weights on the other hand, can be quite difficult to handle since both balance and control are provided solely by the surrounding musculature. The argument comes down to what factor is considered more important to the lifter. Is it more important to develop balance and control by forcing prime mover and stabilizer muscles to maintain these parameters during a free-weight lift, or are the safety, control, and support afforded by a machine a more important factor.

Use controlled resistance training techniques to strengthen the muscles and stabilizers.

Figure 5-9A

Then, train these muscles for balance and control during periods of active recovery.

Figure 5-9B

This need not be an either-or decision. Isolation exercises can be used to strengthen specific muscles, including stabilizers. Once this strength base is developed balance and control can be trained using free-weights under low load conditions. Finally, the weights for both the machine and free-weight lifts can be increased as conditioning improves. An alternative strategy is to utilize controlled resistance training techniques to strengthen the muscles and stabilizers, and then train these muscles for balance and control during periods of active recovery (see Figures 5-9A & B).

The Home vs. the Health Club, Which is Better

Health club memberships can become costly, but so can in-home exercise equipment. As for quality and versatility, the health club offers far more options then any single unit device designed for in-home use. While many in-home machine manufacturers boast that their apparatus is capable of performing many health-club-like exercises, few of them can truly duplicate levels of overload or isolation afforded by individual machines. This is not to say that these machines can not provide a good workout, rather, the argument is that it is virtually impossible for a single machine to be good at everything.

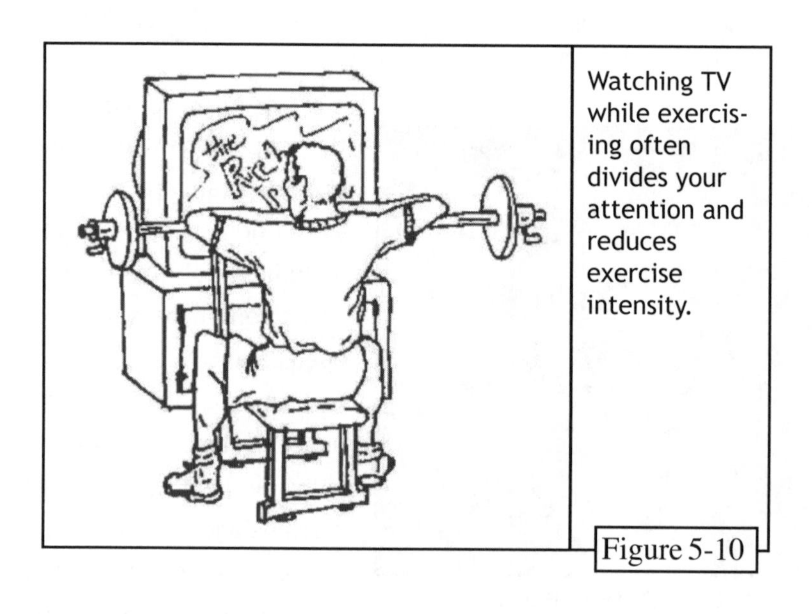

Watching TV while exercising often divides your attention and reduces exercise intensity.

Figure 5-10

A second consideration is based on the balance between convenience and effectiveness of the workout. It's nice to be able to work out in the comfort of your own home, but remember our definition of a workout. For a workout to be effective it must be of sufficient intensity to illicit a change. Watching TV while exercising often divides your attention and reduces exercise intensity (Figure 5-10).

Often the commitment to go to the gym is the first step in the pattern leading to an effective workout. For example, many people prefer a club because it motivates them. A good fitness facility with knowledgeable staff will certainly help you achieve your fitness goals faster then working out on your own. In addition, the social interactions and camaraderie may help you to adhere to your training program.

For many of us the decision to cut a workout short or not to exercise at all is much easier when made in the privacy of our own home. In the final analysis you need to decide the goal of your intended training program and how important variety is in your exercise scheme. One last piece of advice, do your homework before you purchase a machine. If you want to work out at home be sure the machine you purchase will meet your needs and that you will enjoy using it. Otherwise, you may end up with an expensive clothes hanger (the fate of most home exercise machines).

TYPES OF EXERCISE EQUIPMENT

There are many ways in which equipment delivers resistance to the working muscles. You don't need cumbersome machines to provide resistance. In fact, resistance can be easily created by another human being or your own body weight. This is called *manual resistance* and is often employed by coaches, therapists, and trainers during rehabilitation. So why would someone use a machine over manual resistance, their own body weight, or cheaper devices such as elastic tubing or sand bags? The answer lies in the goal of the training program. From rehabilitation to extreme athletic performance, there are a variety of issues that one must examine prior to selecting a training apparatus. The question then is not which is better, but which is better suited for your intended exercise goal.

Free-Weights

Free-weights are the classic form of free-resistance. You see them everywhere from the garage bench set to the lifting platform in the Olympics. There are many types of *free-weights* on the market. *Olympic* plates and barbells are the ones used by most athletes and

Olympic plates and barbells are the free-weights used by most athletes and found in most health clubs.

Figure 5-11

found in most health clubs (see Figure 5-11). They are named Olympic weights because they are similar to the weights used in Olympic lifting. Steel or lead plates are shaped like discs and are coated with either paint or some type of rubber. Rubber plates, or *bumper* plates as they are called in the gym, are designed to sustain the impact of being dropped while preventing damage to both the floor and the weight. These are often used by athletes and Olympic lifters since they can be dropped in case of emergency or at the end point of an exhaustive set.

The most common plate is the poured steel plate. Since the molds for most of the plates used in the health club, weight room, or home are not precise, it is not uncommon for a 45 pound plate to be "off" by a pound or two (see Figure 5-12A). Free-weight plates cost about 30-50 cents per pound for steel and $1.50-$2.00 per pound for rubber (see Figure 5-12B). Olympic bars cost between $75 and $150. However, precision weights (individually made so the weight is exact), such as those used in the Olympics, can cost as much as $6 per pound, and Olympic bars can run from $800-$1200 for a single bar! An Olympic bar is 7 feet long, weighs 45 pounds and has a wider bar diameter at the end (1 1/4 inch) for the plates to fit on (called a "sleeve").

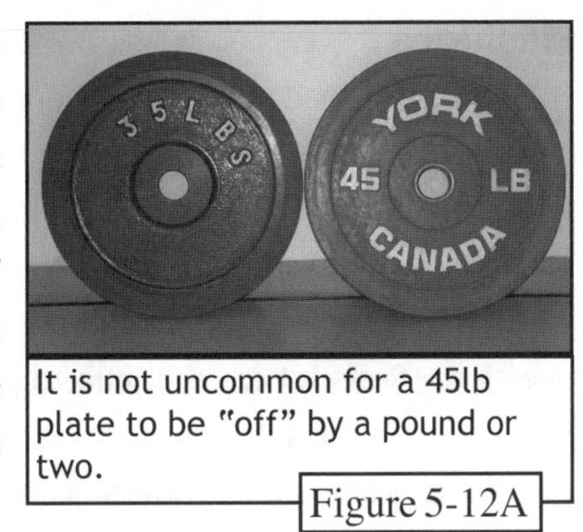

It is not uncommon for a 45lb plate to be "off" by a pound or two.

Figure 5-12A

Free-Weight plates cost about 30-50 cents per pound for steel and $1.50-$2.00 per pound for rubber.

Figure 5-13

Dumbbells come in a variety of shapes and sizes. Some are preset and others are adjustable. Again, like regular weights, the cheaper dumbbells are not as exact in weight. Smaller diameter plates (1/2 inch) are used on standard bars and dumbbells.

There are several kinds of bars designed for a variety of training objectives. One of the most common, other than the straight bar, is the *EZ curl* or *cambered* bar shown in figure 5-14. The bar is designed for comfort and range of motion since it puts the hands in a neutral position rather than fully pronated as would be the case with a straight bar.

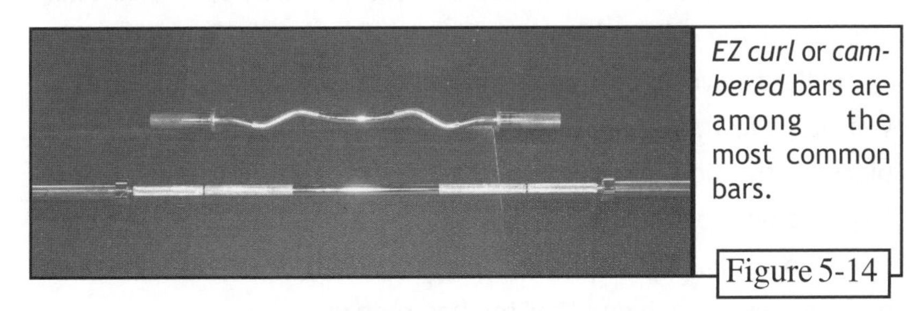

EZ curl or *cambered* bars are among the most common bars.

Figure 5-14

Machines

This is a broad category. There are several kinds of machines, boasting a variety of training advantages. By the time you have finished reading this book, it is certain that a new machine will be on the market. How do you weed through the rhetoric to determine which is best for you? Unfortunately there is no simple answer to this question. Researchers continue to provide information about each machine, and this information can help you match a machine to your specific exercise goals. However, it is still a matter of comfort and personal preference since your willingness to use the machine will affect your willingness to train.

The Cam and Pulley

Two of the most basic machine components described in most physics books are the pulley and the cam. The pulley is a wheel with a grooved circumference that provides a track for a rope, cable, or band to run along. A cam is a distorted cylinder that rides on an axle (see figure 5-15). The shape of a cam can be varied so that it has high and low points that meet the unique requirements of the machine. Cams may also have grooved circumferences to accommodate ropes or cables. So a pulley that is not circular can be called a cam.

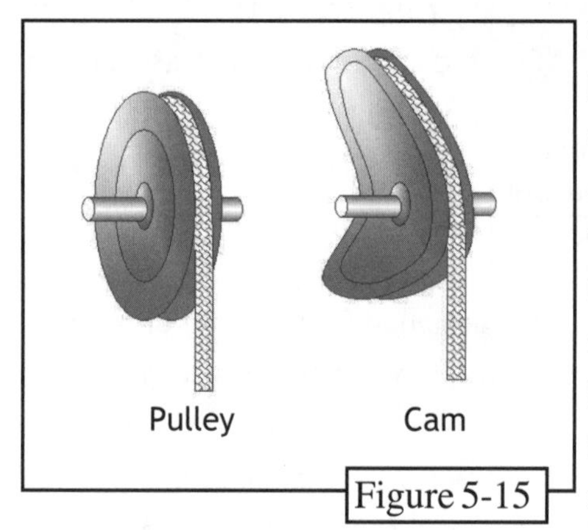

Figure 5-15

Pulleys have been used for years as machines to move heavy weights. We've all seen pictures of workers using pulleys to move a piano up the side of a building. Pulleys are also on the end of the large cranes that are used to move girders and other objects on construction sights. The old clotheslines that many of us remember also had a pulley at each end that the line rode on.

For years, weight training machines, like the classic universal machine, used pulleys to apply resistance for exercises. These were often used when the movement itself would naturally move the weight with gravity, like the lat pull down or standing triceps extension.

In the early 1970s, however, Arthur Jones created a set of resistance training machines that were designed to match the strength curve of each and every individual by simply adjusting the seat or bench to match the stature of the lifter. At the heart of these machines were cams (which at the time were a revolutionary concept). What Jones realized was that by changing the shape of the pulley (making it a cam) he could adjust the working load to the unique length-tension curve (see Chapter 3) of each joint. Jones felt that his cams resembled the shape of a shellfish called the nautilus and thus the Nautilus Machine was born (see Figure 5-16). A number of machines have adapted the cam. The generic name applied to these machines is accommodating resistance machines since their load curves are designed to "accommodate" for the length-tension curve of the joint.

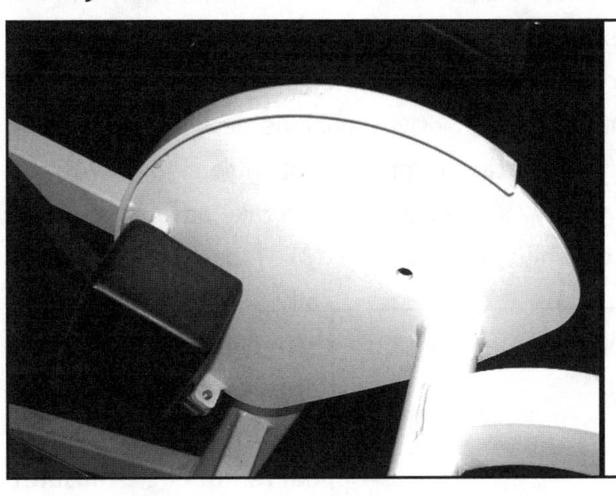

The Nautilus Machine's cams resemble the shape of a shellfish called the nautilus.

Figure 5-16

As discussed in Chapter 3, the relative force generated at any joint is the combined effect of the length of the muscle and the angle of pull by the muscle on the bones of that joint. The cam was designed to accommodate for these factors by modifying the relative leverage (adjusting the relative weight at the hand or foot) during the lift. In theory, this design is very strong. In practice, it is difficult to match everyone's strength curve even using modern technology that allows exacting adjustments of the seats and pads (see figure 5-17).

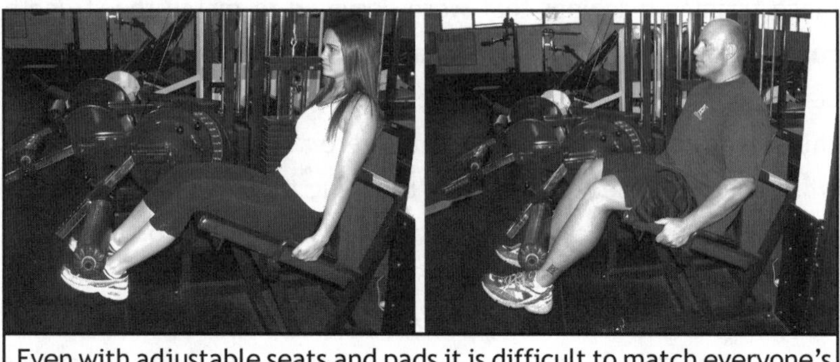

Even with adjustable seats and pads it is difficult to match everyone's strength curve.

Figure 5-17

Regardless of whether the pulley is circular or a cam, pulley systems allow us to move weights against gravity comfortably without having to make extreme changes in body angles or position. This often requires very elaborate pulley systems which are examples of the engineering brilliance that drives machine design. When using these machines it is important to properly align your joint with the pivot point of the pulley to allow the body to take advantage of the machine's unique capability (see Figure 5-18). Today, there are literally hundreds of different cam-pulley systems to help deliver resistance that matches the strength curve of each muscle/ joint.

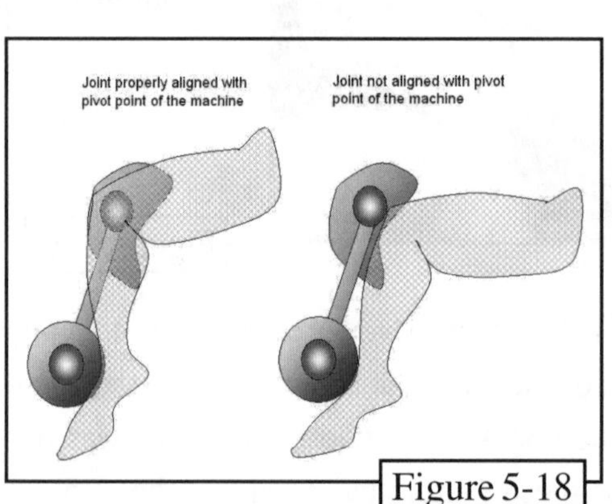

Figure 5-18

Plate Loading Machines vs. Stack Loading

When we think of plates we usually think of the free-weights described above (barbells and dumbbells). However, many machines now utilize plates to apply a resistance. These machines usually incorporate loading posts, similar to those seen at the ends of Olympic bars, which hold the plates. Plate loaded machines allow for virtually limitless resistance to be used. It is rare to see a person use more weight than a plate-loading machine can handle.

Stack machines have a column or stack of weights incorporated as part of the machine. Therefore, these machines have a maximum weight that is provided and set increments dictated by the mass of each weight in the stack. Although the average person will never exceed a "stack", many strength athletes can. The stack and the plate-load systems are both based on the cam-pulley or lever arm systems. When first designed, stack machines could not be operated isolaterally, however, it is now common to find stack machines that do offer this type of training (see Figure 5-19). Several equipment manufacturers have also designed combination cam-pulley and plate loading machines. The proponents of these machines argue that they offer a greater number of movement patterns through more planes of motion than machines with a set movement path. Opponents counter with the argument that these machines are too similar to free-weights. So a new debate has begun, do we lift with machines, free-weights, or machines that

Stack machines have a column or stack of weights incorporated as part of the machine.

Figure 5-19

imitate free-weights! Figure 5-20 shows examples of a plate loading, a stack, and a combination machine.

Plate loading machine

Stack machine

Combination machine

Figure 5-20

Hydraulic Machines

The term hydraulic refers to the movement of liquids. Hydraulic machines create resistance using liquid filled chambers or pistons. As you push against the piston the fluid is forced through the chamber and pressure builds creating resistance. As the movement continues, and the liquid becomes less compressible, the resistance increases. Adjustable hydraulic machines allow the lifter to have more control of the resistance setting. The main advantage of the hydraulic system is that the initial resistance can be set very low (for people with limited strength) and the equipment itself is very lightweight. A disadvantage is that it is difficult to quantify the resistance in kilograms which is easily done when using stack machines or free-weights.

A number of peculiarities exist with hydraulic machines. First of all, since the resistance is dictated by a fluid, the speed at which the individual moves affects the amount of resistance. This means that the faster you move the more "drag" you create (see Figure 5-21). Second, in many hydraulic systems the eccentric portion of the movement becomes very easy since the liquid is merely refilling the piston. Therefore, the strength curve is nearly nonexistent during the eccentric portion of the movement. Even the push-pull hydraulic machines (as typically used for pace workouts - described in Chapter 8) don't provide an eccentric component. They are concentric-concentric using independent cylinders for each direction. In other words, if a chest press is being performed against the cylinder on one side, a seated row will be performed against the

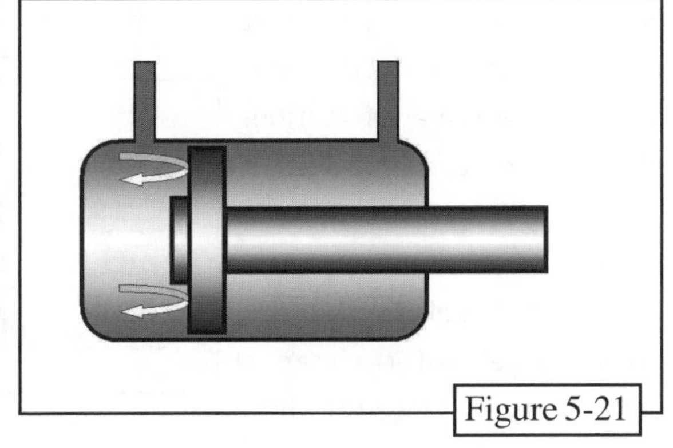

Figure 5-21

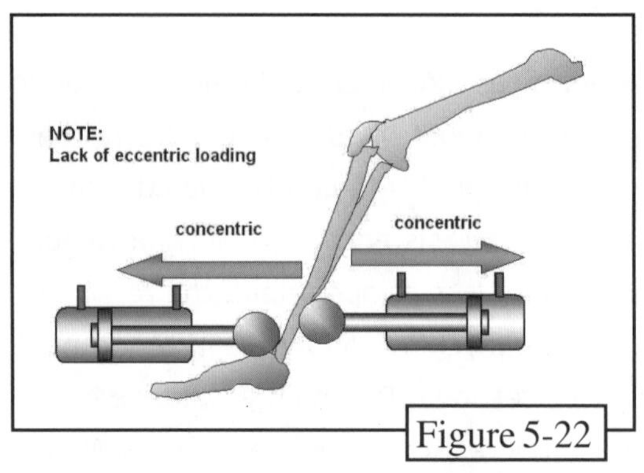

Figure 5-22

cylinder on the other. While this is effective at concentrically training both antagonistic muscles, the important eccentric portion of the movement is virtually nonexistent (see Figure 5-22).

Air-Driven (Pneumatic) Machines

Pneumatic machines are machines that use compressed gas (usually air) rather than liquid to produce resistance. They can be divided into two types 1) those using compressed air cylinder and depending on pressure increases to generate resistance; and 2) air-gathering machines that function by slowly redistributing air through gathering chambers.

The first type, which uses cylinders, suffers from the same inherent problem as hydraulic systems. The pressure, and therefore resistance, continually increases through the range of motion. This situation certainly doesn't match the typical length-force pattern seen at most joints. These machines also provide different levels of resistance depending on the speed at which you move (see Figure 5-23).

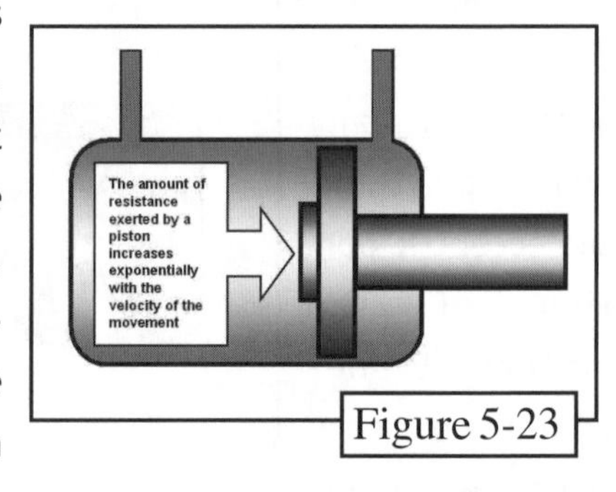

Figure 5-23

To address this problem, air-gathering machines were developed. The pioneer and primary producer of these machines is the Keiser Corporation. The machines gather air, redistributes it through holes or orifices that slow down its flow and create resistance, then release the air as necessary rather than just compressing it (see Figure 5-24). The pressure in the chamber can therefore match the strength curve. This redistribution of air allows the resistance to remain stable

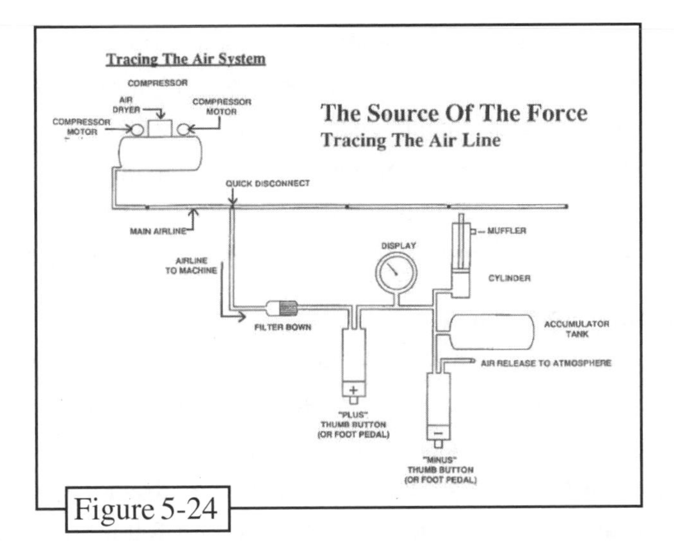

Figure 5-24

throughout the range of motion. In addition, since air can be pumped into or removed from the chamber, the amount of resistance can be adjusted to match the individual's strength or power capacity. And finally, this equipment allows resistance to be offered in very small increments. This makes the machines attractive to older individuals and beginners who require more controlled increases in overload, while still offering efficient overload to more advanced lifters (see Figure 5-25).

Air-Driven machines are attractive to older individuals and beginners who require more controlled increases in overload.

Figure 5-25

In addition, the stable length-tension curve and low inertia make these machines ideal for power training since they allow high-speed movements under constant resistance with a much lower potential for injury than would be expected with weight-stack machines or free-weights. The disadvantage of these machines is that a separate air compressor and an air hose system are needed for them to function. A second shortcoming, which is more psychological than physical, is that many lifters can't adjust to the lack of inertia, and they miss the "clanking" that accompanies pushing steel. It should be noted that each machine is independent, and the system is extremely low-pressure so it is not dangerous.

Graphite Flex Rods

The flex rod system was popularized by Bowflex and delivers resistance that can be increased or decreased by using more or fewer rods (see Figure 5-26). Much like a fishing pole, when the resistance rod bends, it creates a greater resistance. The advantage of this system is that the rod's bending action is set to follow the strength curve. Another advantage of this system is that the range of motion, lifting angle, and control are completely dependent on the individual lifter. While many strength practitioners argue that the machine does not produce adequate resistance, many of the machines can add additional flex rods that provide resistance that far surpasses the ability of most people.

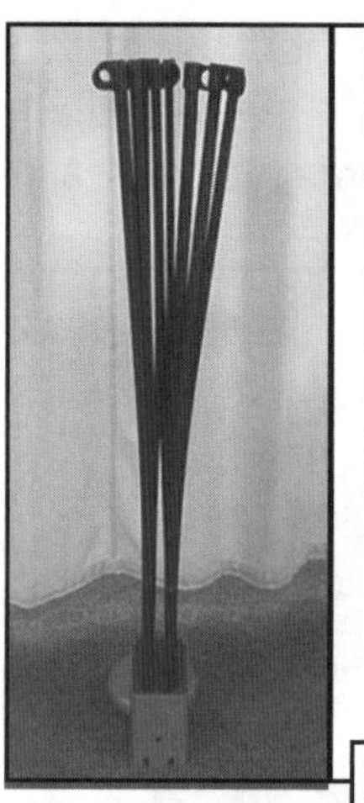

Flex rod systems deliver resistance that can be increased or decreased by using more or fewer rods.

Figure 5-26

These machines try to simulate many of the single exercise machines found in a health club into an all-in-one system. While many exercises are quite effective, no machine is truly capable of doing everything, and some muscle groups and movements are more effectively targeted than others. Since these machines have a cable and pulley design, they do allow exercise in almost unlimited planes and through large ranges of motion. As noted earlier, the cable and pulley system also requires the use of accessory muscles to stabilize the working joints, and this requirement is further increased by the freedom of movement of the rods themselves. Given their nearly unlimited planes of motion during many of the exercises, the need to employ accessory muscles as well as the prime movers, and the capacity to work at various speeds in the force-velocity spectrum, these machines are becoming highly respected for "functional" movement training.

Rubber Resistance Weight Straps

Similar to the flex rods, rubber straps (or "elastomers" in the industry) act very much like springs (see Figure 5-27). As the band is stretched, resistance is increased. To increase the overall tension created, these machines allow multiple straps or thicker straps to be used. Elastomer-based machines are often designed to closely control the path or movement of the lever arms and, therefore, don't provide the freedom of movement of rod-loaded machines. Also, many experts argue that the elastomers work like elastic bands and, therefore, excessively load the exercise at the end of the range of motion. You will commonly see this type of resistance offered in the smaller home exercise devices seen on television.

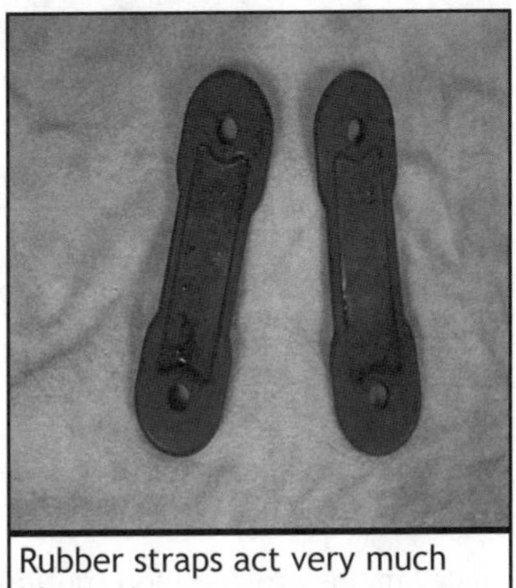

Rubber straps act very much like springs.

Figure 5-27

Isokinetic Devices

A true *isokinetic* machine is usually connected to a computer interface that allows the user to set the limits (see Figure 5-28). As described earlier, an isokinetic device sets the speed at which the lifter will work. The lifter pushes maximally throughout the entire range of motion thus truly and effectively matching the strength curve. The advantages are unparalleled in terms of isolating a specific muscle and developing force at a set speed of movement. However, the

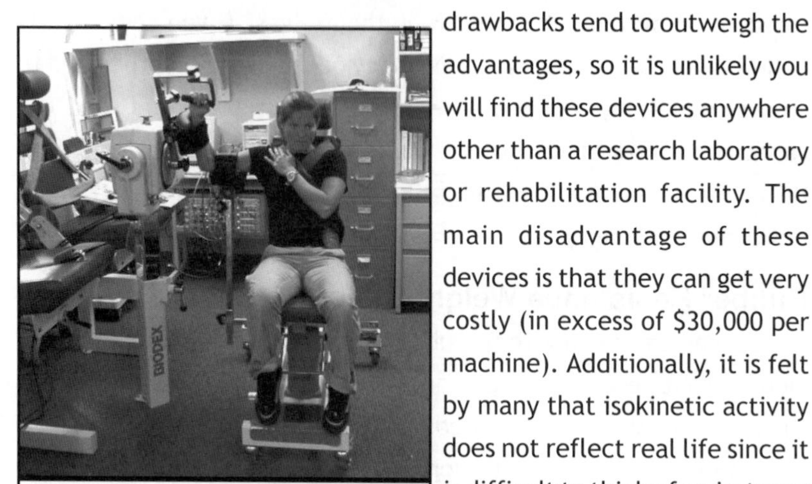

A isokinetic machine is usually connected to a computer interface that allows the the user to set limits.

Figure 5-28

drawbacks tend to outweigh the advantages, so it is unlikely you will find these devices anywhere other than a research laboratory or rehabilitation facility. The main disadvantage of these devices is that they can get very costly (in excess of $30,000 per machine). Additionally, it is felt by many that isokinetic activity does not reflect real life since it is difficult to think of an instance when we would produce maximal force throughout an entire movement while the speed of that movement is held constant.

Bands

Band training is becoming more popular. Although both bands and elastomer resistance machines use elastic tension to apply resistance, bands provide more options. They require no machinery and can be attached to a bar or other implement such as a handle, bat, or racket to apply resistance to simulated sport or other functional movements (see Figure 5-29).

Bands provide more options since they require no machinery.

Figure 5-29

Heavy resistance training advocates, such as power lifters, have begun using thick bands wrapped around the ends of bars during a movement (see Figure 5-30). Since the band delivers a greater resistance as it is stretched, this type of training is of particular interest to those wishing to increase the resistance at the end of a movement. While this is not needed by most, it may serve to help train the lockout portion of the lift (often a source of frustration for power lifters). On the non-competitive side, bands present a nice challenge and allow for an unlimited number of exercises in every plane of motion. In addition they provide a safe method for performing high speed movement, especially effective for power development. Again, quantifying the actual resistance is still something of a mystery.

Thick bands wrapped around the ends of bars are used to increase the resistance at the end of a movement.

Figure 5-30

Tubes

Surgical tubing has been used for years during rehabilitation. More recently it has been popularized and become part of the training community. Commercially made tubes are color coded to indicate the level of resistance they provide. Many have handles or bars to which they are attached. Therefore, tubes provide the benefits of bands with the "feel" and feedback of weights. The thickness of the tube determines its overall resistance. Again, like the other elastic devices, they provide almost limitless boundaries in range of motion and movement speed (see Figure 5-31).

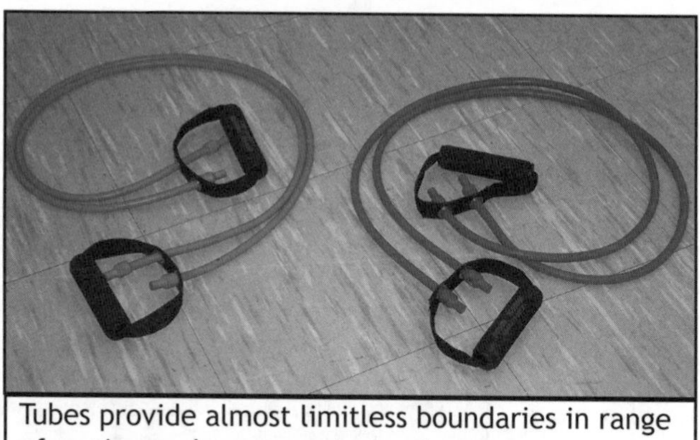

Tubes provide almost limitless boundaries in range of motion and movement speed.

Figure 5-31

Medicine and SWISS Balls

Finally, "Med Balls" have become a mainstay for many athletic training programs. Their use is now trickling down to the general population and "core" training programs are now popping up in many gyms and fitness facilities (see Figure 5-32). They provide a stimulating challenge, can be used to effectively train the stretch-shortening cycle, and above all, can be released at the end of a high-speed movement without injury or damage to anyone or anything. This final point is particularly attractive for developing power as you will see in Chapter 10. In addition to medicine balls which are lifted or thrown, larger, inflatable balls, often called SWISS balls, are used to build strength and core stability as well as train balance (see Figure 5-33).

Advocates claim that attempting to lift a weight while being supported by a ball requires specific development of the abdominals

Medicine Balls have become a mainstay for many athletic training programs.

Figure 5-32

and *core* or trunk musculature. While this may be the case, there is little conclusive evidence showing that this type of training improves overall performance. Certainly such exercises do require a degree of balance; however, opponents argue that ball training is not reflective of real life since almost all activity in daily life requires force to be produced by the legs driving against the ground. Regardless of your take on the subject, SWISS ball training challenges both stability and balance and can provide a fun alternative to traditional weight training.

SWISS balls are used to build strength and core stability as well as train ballance.

Figure 5-33

Shaking Things Up

We would be remiss if we left this chapter without mentioning one of the latest innovations in resistance training, the use of vibration to increase overload. We've all seen construction workers using jack hammers or riders hanging on to a Harley Davidson as it tools down the road. Both scenarios conjure pictures of vibrating muscles. A number of studies have incorporated vibrating platforms, dumbbells, and other devises to add vibration to resistance training regimens, and the results have been very promising. In all cases, muscle activity during the training was greater when vibration was added to the overload and power was increased to a greater degree in the vibration versus the non-vibration condition.

The Equipment Solution

The answer to the question of which piece of weight training equipment is best is easy. There is no "best" piece. Each piece of equipment we have presented has its own place in a general scheme to improve performance, fitness, and health. Generally speaking, when starting out, it is best to use machines and then progress to free weights. Other forms of equipment may be used during specific training cycles (see Chapters 9 and 10) or to provide variety to your training program. Results of certain sport-specific, rehabilitation, and population-specific programs may be maximized by the use of particular pieces of equipment; however, an overall program can be designed using even the most basic type of equipment. In fact, overload can be effectively provided by such manual labor tasks as lifting and carrying objects, working with picks and shovels, or laying bricks; but few of us have the opportunity or inclination to do these things so the gym or weight room provides a more enjoyable alternative.

Chapter

6

The Exercises

Perhaps one of the most difficult decisions for recreational lifters, personal trainers, and strength and conditioning coaches to make is the selection of the "right" exercises. Truth be told, there are no right, and for that matter, no wrong exercises. Essentially, exercise selection, while it does follow a scientific pattern, is largely a matter of preference and desired outcome. This does not mean that it doesn't matter what exercises you do, rather, it means that you will have several choices that you can make in reaching your goals. There are hundreds of different exercises, at times, ten or more per body part! To make matters more confusing, there may be hundreds of different ways to apply resistance during those exercises. If you think back to the different training methods outlined in Chapter 4 and multiply them by the myriad of exercises you will learn in this chapter, you can see that you have a huge selection from which you can draw when you design a workout.

Without a doubt the most important consideration, after you have chosen the resistance training exercises, is proper form and execution of the chosen exercises. To master proper technique we advise that your initial lifting pattern follow a controlled repetition pattern of about 2 seconds for the concentric and 3 seconds for the eccentric. Once your technique is perfected, rep speed rep number, and set schemes can be manipulated depending on your fitness goals.

If you look through fitness magazines or go to a health club, you have probably seen dozens of variations of the same basic exercises. While research exists supporting the use of some of the variations, most of these so-called "new exercises" are only supported by anecdotal claims. Additionally, in the majority of the studies that have compared these variations to the "old favorites" presented in this chapter, the old favorites have proven superior. Simply put, most exercises come from one of the major movements described in this text. But before we present these "basic" exercises lets look at some fundamental guidelines.

First, the body can be divided into 6 parts: the upper anterior, or front, including the arms; upper posterior, or back, including the arms; middle anterior; middle posterior; lower anterior, or thighs and shins; and lower posterior, or hamstrings and calves. Within each of these areas, the body can be further subdivided into muscle groups, individual muscles and specific fiber bundles within a muscle. However, if you were to perform 6 basic exercises, essentially you could work your entire body. Of course, if this were all it really took to get in shape then the multi-billion-dollar fitness industry would have crumbled 50 years ago.

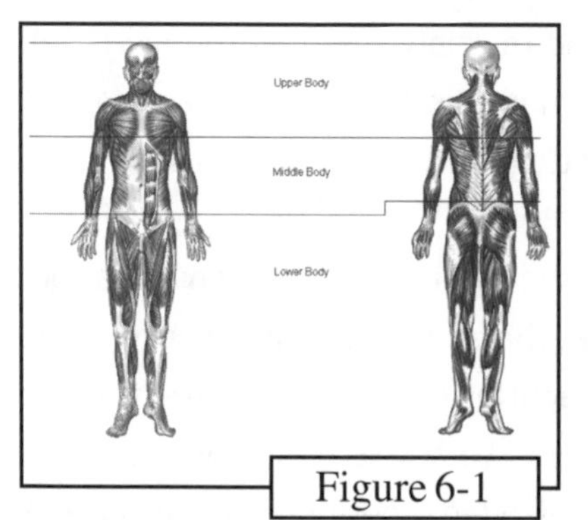

Figure 6-1

Exercises can be grouped by action, movement, muscle group, or the number of joints used during the exercise.

When grouped by action we typically use terms like pushing (referring to exercises that push the load away from the body) or pulling (referring to exercises where the load is pulled toward the body). When grouped by movement, we use the terms that you learned in the chapter on biomechanics, flexion (joint angle closing) and extension (joint angle opening). You may hear the terms open or closed chain. Open chain exercises are those where the terminal end of the body part being exercised is free to move, for example during a knee extension. A closed chain exercise is when that terminal end is held in position so that the rest of the body moves, for example during a squat.

When grouped by muscle, we refer to exercises by the muscle or the muscle group they target. For example, we speak of an exercise as being a "pec" (pectoralis) or "tri" (triceps) exercise because it focuses on that specific muscle. Exercises of this nature may be isolated to the single muscle or include several muscles within a movement. We also use the terms concentric and eccentric, which you will recall refer to the shortening and lengthening of a muscle, respectively.

The final grouping, by joint, usually classifies exercises by the joint used, but more recently, has also concentrated on the number of joints used when performing a specific exercise. For example, we often refer to exercises as being single joint (movements about 1 joint) or multi-joint (movements involving more than 1 joint).

Of course, the obvious question becomes "what should I do?" While the answer to this question is not absolute, we do have some guidelines and much of the decision is dictated by the specific needs of the individual. This means that a bodybuilder (looking for muscle hypertrophy) has a very different training regime than a soccer player (looking for muscular endurance). It also means that the muscles they target and how they train them are very different. While many recreational lifters start out training to gain size, it is becoming increasingly more popular to train specific actions or movements for athletic and functional success. To this end, we have chosen to list exercises by body area and then include several exercises that work the entire body or require the synchronized action of the entire body during their performance. Building specific programs will be discussed in chapter 10.

While there are many ways to select exercises, the two most common methods are by time availability and by need. While it is probably obvious that the second factor (need) is far more desirable, the first factor (time availability) is more often employed. To help guide your selection process we have provided the following:

Exercise Feel and Comfort

One of the most important considerations when you begin a lifting program is your comfort and enjoyment. While the exercise should stress the targeted muscles and provide sufficient overload, it should not be painful. Training that causes pain, often indicates too much intensity or volume of work done in too short of time period. Remember, pain is the result of muscle damage and can increase with subsequent workouts. If this damage does not escalate to a level where it prevents you from exercising, it may certainly cause you to avoid exercise or classify it as an unpleasant experience.

Specific Range of Motion

Does the exercise target the range and plane of motion desired? For example, an athlete may need to work on certain rotational motions, while a senior citizen might concentrate on total body movements that would be more effective at increasing mobility and preventing falls.

Targeting Specific Muscles

This concept is fairly obvious, but often exercises are incorrectly chosen. Prior to selecting an exercise, you should consider what exercises best isolate the muscle. Second, you may wish to determine the risk factors associated with each exercise. For instance, many exercises, like the behind the neck lat pull down, have been highly touted as being highly effective (in this case at isolating the upper back muscles), yet have been proven to be highly risky.

Time/"Bang for Buck"

A fourth consideration is time. Often people do not exercise because they "don't have time". However, this "time" excuse can be addressed in a number of ways. For example, multi-joint movements save time, as does circuit training. When time is limited, it is best to select exercises that work the greatest number of muscles per movement, are easy to adjust as far as load and body position, and are relatively easy to perform so that skill and technique are not compromised.

Skill/Technique

The final guideline to consider when selecting exercises is the level of skill necessary to perform the exercises chosen. Many lifting techniques require extensive skill and technique training before they can be performed safely and effectively. For example, free-weights, particularly dumbbells, require greater skill to control the weight as it moves through multiple planes of motion while machines dictate a fixed line of movement. Additionally, multi-joint movements such as power cleans require both skill and timing which can only be developed with practice. Remember, proper exercise execution is vital for overall program success. We recommend that the beginning lifter first master easier exercises before progressing to the more difficult movements.

A final note on exercise selection: there is a long-standing debate whether free weights or machines should be used. It is tempting to suggest that machine exercises suit a particular population (such as a senior vs. adolescent) more than free weights (typically used by athletes); however the decision should be based on a number of factors such as:

1. The current medical status of the individual including his or her risk factors based on cardiovascular, skeletal, metabolic, and neuromuscular health issues;

2. Current training status as it relates to muscle and connective tissue strength and flexibility;

3. Ability of the subject to effectively control the movement under specific loading conditions;

4. Factors such as training volume, load, movement speed and movement complexity that may affect both the effectiveness and safety of the movement;

5. Availability of workout partners to act as spotters during the workout.

Free weights and machines are both effective lifting modalities, however they may produce different effects and may differ in their ability to target specific needs and goals. Therefore, it is recommended that using a combination of both may yield the greatest gains.

The exercises described in this chapter target the major muscles of the body. Since there are several hundred variations of these exercises, the following points should be considered with each description:

a) Each exercise could be performed with machines, barbells, dumbbells, and any other form of resistance that allows you to use the same movement pattern.

b) The complete range of motion described is necessary regardless of modality to train all of the muscles in the movement across their entire range of contractility.

c) Proper technique is essential.

d) Breathe while you lift - exhale during the exertion phase (concentric or positive) inhale during the return phase (eccentric or negative).

The Lifting-Specific Position

In sport, coaches refer to the "Sport Specific or Sport Ready Position" to ensure that an athlete is ready to react, move and/or be ready take a hit. That same position, for the most part, is also the proper position that should be employed by every person performing every resistance exercise. As we have already stated, using proper technique and maintaining proper body position during each exercise will not only reduce the risk of injury, it will also improve the overall effectiveness of the exercise. The following are the key concepts for proper body position during lifting:

1. Always look forward, keeping your head and chin up but do not hyper-extend your neck.

2. Keep your chest out and lower back flat or slightly arched

(along its normal lordotic curve).

3. There should be a slight bend at both your knees and waist when performing standing exercises. When sitting or lying, your feet should be firmly planted on the ground.

4. Your body weight should be borne by your heels (rather than your toes as in the "sport-specific" position). Position your feet slightly wider than shoulder-width and a slightly staggered foot position is strongly recommended for maximizing balance.

5. Always lock your thumbs around the barbell, dumbbell, or cable handle and keep your wrists as straight as possible.

THE EXERCISES

Chest/Pushes/Upper Anterior Movements

Flat Bench Press

The bench press (figure 6-2) is considered the king of upper body exercises. This exercise requires a great deal of skill and focus. The major muscles worked are the chest, shoulder and triceps (pectoralis major, anterior deltoid, and triceps brachii).

Figure 6-2a

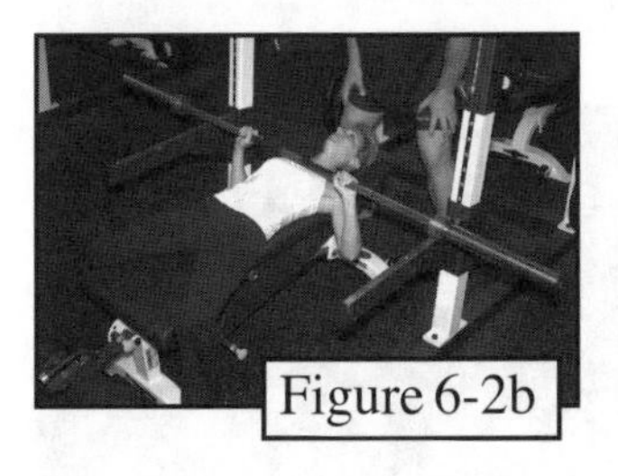

Figure 6-2b

Body Position

The lift is performed while lying in a prone position on a flat bench. To ensure the proper position, once on your back, align your eyes underneath the bar. Keep your head in a neutral position. Grab the bar with a grip slightly wider than shoulder width apart. Place your feet flat on the ground and keep your buttocks in contact with the bench for the entire movement. Maintaining a natural lordotic curve will help reduce the strain on the lower back. Maintain these key points throughout the entire lift, especially as you fatigue.

Performance

Lift the bar from the bench uprights and pause for a moment. Take a deep breath then slowly allow the bar to descend (eccentric) toward the nipple level. Avoid bouncing at the chest, rather, there should be a slight pause. Begin the ascent (concentric) by "driving" the bar up forcefully. Make sure to exhale as you push the bar up. Gently lock the arms out at the top. Finish the exercise by re-racking the bar. These same muscles can be worked using the machine chest press (see Figure 6-3); however, because the machine controls the movement, the use of accessory muscles is reduced.

Figure 6-3a

Figure 6-3b

Variation

The incline bench press requires the upper portion of the pectoral muscles and medial deltoids to work a little harder than the flat bench as you might expect if you remember the vector lifting model we presented in Chapter 2. The triceps and anterior deltoids are also involved. Adjust the bench to about a 45 degree angle. As the angle increases, the activity levels of the other muscles are also affected. The triceps show similar activity levels compared to the flat bench; however, the anterior and medial deltoids become more active as the

Figure 6-4

weight moves to a more overhead position. Perform the exercise the same way as you would during a flat bench. The bar or machine handles should travel down toward the collarbone (see Figure 6-4). For a greater range of motion during the lift, use dumbbells (see Figure 6-5).

Figure 6-5

Pec Flys

This single-joint exercise isolates the pectoralis muscles and provides a greater range of motion than the bench press or chest press at the shoulder joint. While the triceps are not involved dynamically, the anterior deltoids and muscles of the rotator cuff are very active as accessory muscles during this lift.

Position

Figure 6-6a

When using a fly (or pec deck) machine, bend your elbows to form a 90-degree angle. Place your forearms up against the pad (see Figure 6-6). When lying on a bench using dumbbells or a cable, put a slight bend in the arm and hold the handles with a thumb-locked grip and palms facing in. Keep your head/chin up and chest out, maintaining a tight torso throughout the movement (see Figure 6-7).

Figure 6-6b

Performance

To begin the exercise, simultaneously bring both arms together, as if hugging a big bear. Hold the contracted position for a moment before slowly returning to the starting point. Don't allow the weight stack to come crashing back down. Keep the movement slow and controlled. When dumbbells are used, this exercise is called the Dumbbell Fly and requires considerably greater control and additional balance.

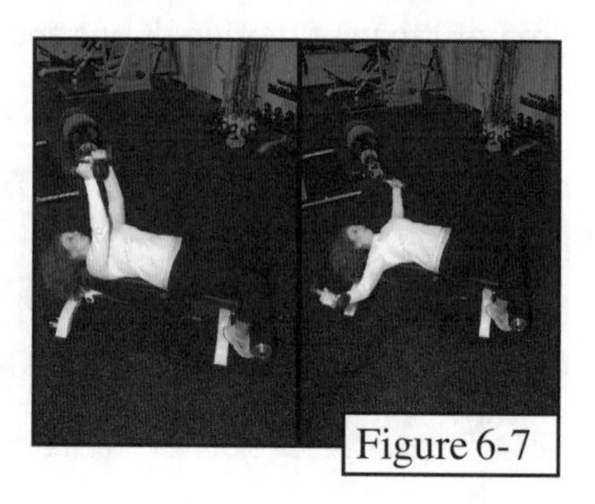

Figure 6-7

Variation

The dumbbell or lying cable peck fly can be done on an incline (similar to the incline bench press) to increase usage of the upper pectoralis and anterior and medial deltoids (see Figure 6-8). However, another popular variation known as the cable crossover, reduces much of the anterior deltoid effect and further isolates the pectoralis major (see Figure 6-9). This exercise is performed by standing, raising your arms out to your sides (abducting) until they are parallel to the floor. Grab the set of high handles from the cable machine and with a slight bend in your arm, pull the handles toward your waist (adduct) ending with your palms touching slightly in front of your hips. Return back to the starting position under control.

Figure 6-8a

Figure 6-8b

Figure 6-9

Parallel Dips

Few exercises can top the parallel dip as a triceps dominated pushing movement (see Figure 6-10). The shoulder and chest also receive their share of work.

Position

For the parallel dip, stand between a set of parallel bars. Lift up on the bars with your arms extended down to the sides. Pull your heels up to your buttocks (or to 90 degrees) or allow them to hang as long as they do not contact the floor. Keep your chest and torso tight.

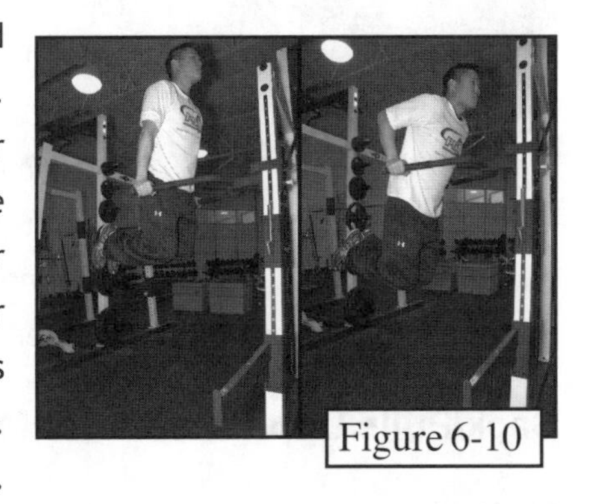
Figure 6-10

For the triceps pushdown, align yourself in the machine so that the elbows are completetly flexed with minimal shoulder elevation.

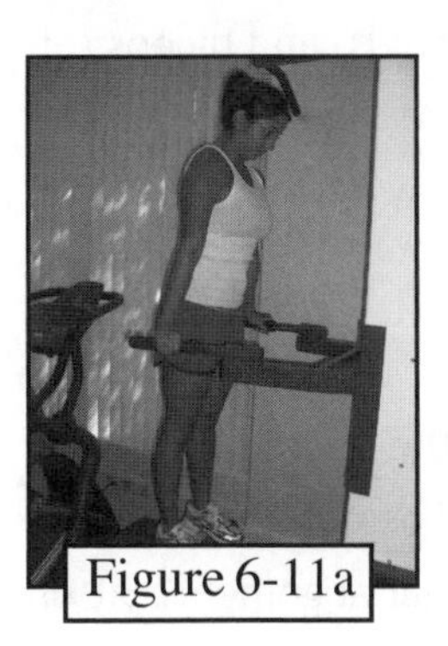
Figure 6-11a

Performance

Slowly lower your body by bending at the elbows. Keep your head in line with your body and do not round your back. Once your arms reach a 90- degree

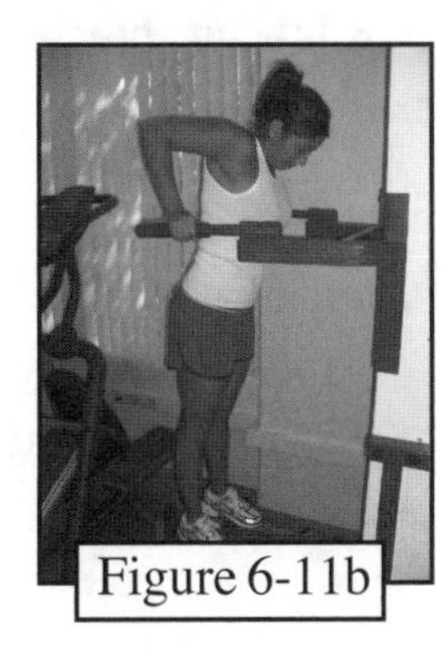
Figure 6-11b

angle, push back up. This exercise requires a base of strength in order to lift your body weight. If this is not possible, use a dip assisted machine found in most gyms (see figure 6-11). You can also do negative only reps until you have built up your strength.

Variation

A bench dip is great for those who cnnot lift their own body weight (see Figure 6-12). Sit on the end of a bench and put your hands down beside and press into the bench. Walk your feet forward and pull your buttocks away from the bench a few inches so you are balanced on your feet and hands. Using the same form bend you arms lowering your buttocks toward the ground. Press back up extending your arms. By moving your feet further or closer from the bench, you will increase or reduce "your body weight".

Figure 6-12b

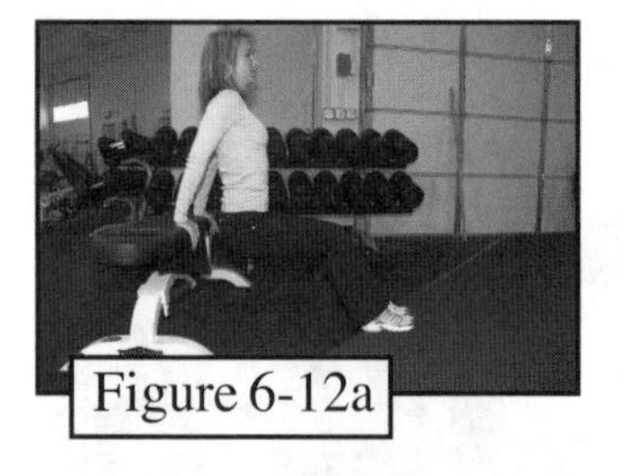
Figure 6-12a

Back/Pulls/Upper Posterior Movements

Seated Row

This exercise emphasizes all of the muscles that allow you to move your arms backwards, thereby working the upper back (lats, teres major, middle and upper traps, and rhomboids) and biceps (biceps brachii, brachialis and brachoradialis) (see Figure 6-13). The exercise can also be performed using a seated row machine (see Figure 6-14).

Position

Proper body positioning is crucial during the seated row. Your back should be slightly arched, the chest should be out and the head should be up. Maintain a neutral head and spinal alignment. Sit on

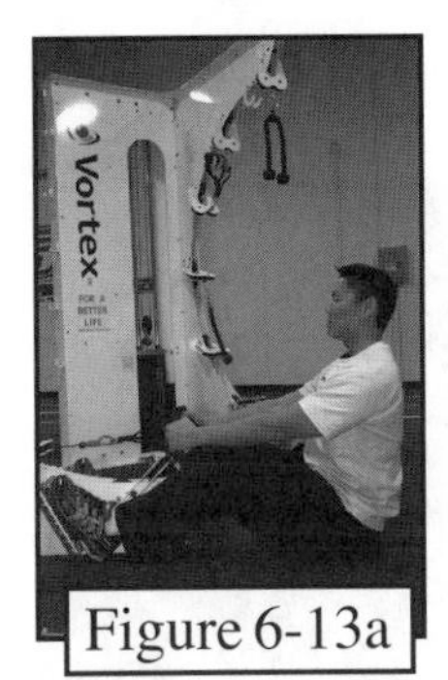

Figure 6-13a

the bench/floor or at the machine. Extend the legs forward placing the feet on the footplate. Maintain a slight bend of the knees. Hold the cable or machine handles with your arms out in front of you. If you are using a seated row machine the seat is typically adjusted so that the chest pad is centered on your sternum. The handles are placed in a position where they can be comfortably grasped with the arms extended completely forward.

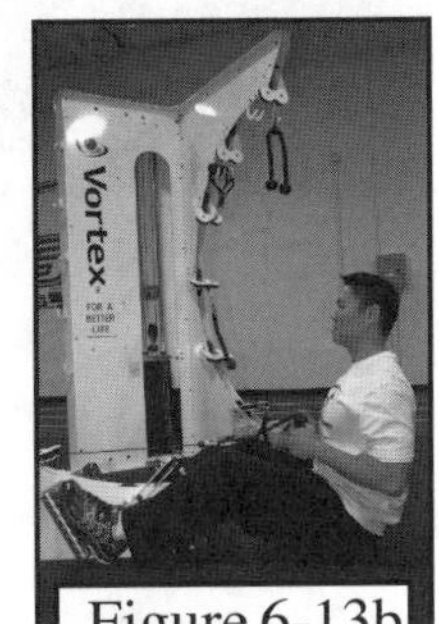

Figure 6-13b

Figure 6-14

Performance

Begin by pulling the elbows back toward the body. Keep your elbows tight at your sides. Pause slightly when the bar reaches your upper abdomen or the handles are pulled to your body. Slowly return to the starting position. The weight is too heavy if you need to use your lower back (extension) to initiate the movement. When using the seated row machine lifters often lean back to complete the exercise, once again this indicates that the weight should be reduced to increase concentration on the back muscles.

Variation

A High Row uses the same motion but emphasizes the rear deltoids, rhomboids and traps by flaring the elbows out to the side

Figure 6-15a

(see Figure 6-15). Keep the same body position and pull the bar or handles to your chest. This will require a little more strength and tighter body position, and is a great exercise for increasing rear deltoid strength.

Figure 6-15b

Lat Pulldowns

Pulldowns work the same muscles but reduce the effect on the rear deltoids and traps. Many consider this exercise the best at targeting lat development.

Figure 6-16a

Position

When using a typical pulley and cable system (see Figure 6-16), secure your lower body tightly under the thigh pad. Grasp the bar with a pronated (palms forward) grip about 1.5 times wider than shoulder width. The same basic position is true when using a solid arm lat pulldown machine, except that you grasp the machine handles (see Figure 6-17).

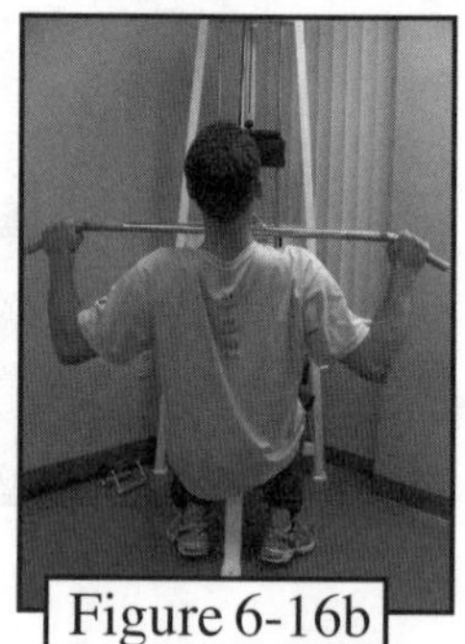
Figure 6-16b

Figure 6-17a

Performance

Lean back slightly and pull the bar to your clavicle by passing close to your face and chin. This front position has

Figure 6-17b

been shown to reduce injury and activate the lats more than other positions such as the behind the neck pulldown. Squeeze the shoulder blades together and keep your chest out and up through the lift. Pause for a moment touching the upper chest, then slowly return to the top. Pulldowns can be performed with a variety of different handles, keep in mind the same guidelines apply.

Variations

Figure 6-18a

The Chin/Pull-Up is a time tested exercise and one of the best muscular strength and endurance builders (see Figure 6-18). For many, performing even a single rep is quite challenging but practicing this exercise will allow you to do these on-demand! Grasp the bar with palms facing in (chin-up variation) or away (pull-up variation) at shoulder width or slightly closer. From this hanging position, pull yourself up toward the bar. Focus on pulling your elbow down and back while squeezing your shoulder blades together as you rise. A true full rep is one where your chin clears the bar. Pause at the top momentarily. Slowly lower back to the starting point. Don't swing and jerk the legs to help get you up. This same exercise can be performed using a resistance-assisted pull-up (see Figure 6-19).

Figure 6-18b

Figure 6-19a

Figure 6-19b

Push/Shoulders

Military Press

A true classic exercise for exhibiting great strength, the military press primarily works the anterior and medial heads of the deltoid and triceps muscles. It can be performed sitting or standing, using machines, barbells or dumbbells. Focus, balance and coordination are important to the success of the lift. The seated version is recommended for beginners and those with certain limitations.

Figure 6-20a

Position

If starting with a barbell, have someone hand off the barbell at arms fully extended (see Figure 6-20). Keep the core of your body stable and your feet firmly on the ground for stabilization. When using dumbbells, sit on a bench and grab a pair of dumbbells (see Figure 6-21). Hoist them up to shoulder level; your palms should be facing forward.

Figure 6-20b

Figure 6-21a

Performance

When using dumbbells, start by raising both arms up at the same time. Your arms should travel in an arc over your head. There is no need to bang the dumbbells hard at the top. Slowly lower the dumbbells back to the original position. If using a barbell, lower the bar to your clavicle, in front of your chin. Elbow placement affects what areas of the deltoids get the most work.

Figure 6-21b

Flaring out the elbows emphasizes the middle deltoids, while bringing them in front of the body works the anterior deltoids to a greater extent. As you begin to fatigue, resist excessively arching your back, as this places unnecessary strain on the lumbar discs.

Figure 6-22a

Variations

Since this is a shoulder exercise, it is possible that that it can be performed at other angles given the range of motion of the shoulder joint. For extra deltoid work, there are 3 isolated exercises that effectively work each of the deltoid heads. The Lateral and Front Raise exercises are highly effective for isolating the middle and anterior deltoids respectively (see Figures 6-22 and 6-23). They can be performed seated or standing. Sit on a bench holding a pair of dumbbells in each hand at yours sides with palms facing your body for a lateral raise and facing backward for the front raise; slowly raise your arms out to the sides (lateral raise) or out in front (front raise). Keep the elbows slightly bent. Raise your arms until they are parallel to the ground. Pause at the top position and slowly return back down. If you are performing the standing version maintain strict form. Avoid any movements with the trunk to assist in completing repetitions as fatigue sets in.

Figure 6-22b

Figure 6-23a

Figure 6-23b

The posterior deltoids are probably one of the most under-trained parts of the body and are difficult to isolate. To perform Rear Delt Flys, lie on a bench face down (see Figure 6-24). Hold the arms down

Figure 6-24a

toward the ground while holding a pair of dumbbells. Keep the weight from touching the floor. Thumbs should be pointing toward each other, slowly raise the arms out to the side until they are parallel to the ground. Squeeze tightly at the top and slowly allow the weights to descend back down. Lateral Raises can also be performed on a lateral raise machine (see Figure 6-25).

Figure 6-24b

Figure 6-25a

Figure 6-25b

ISOLATION ARM EXERCISES

Biceps

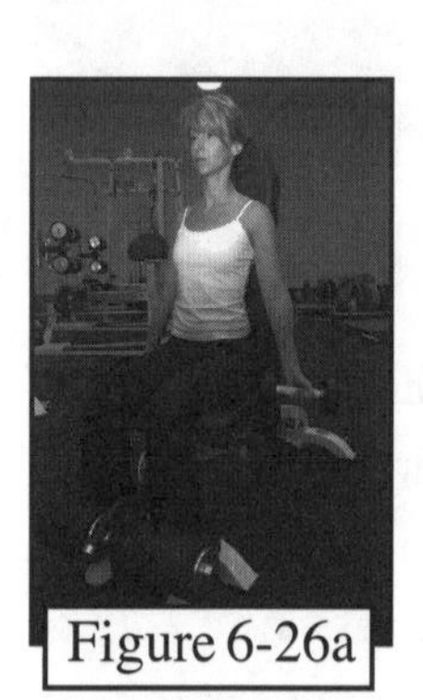
Figure 6-26a

Biceps Curl

Perhaps the most common exercise on the planet is the biceps curl. It will target the biceps and forearms effectively. This exercise can be done seated or standing with a barbell, dumbbell or machine.

Figure 6-26b

Position

Hold a pair of dumbbells down at your sides with palms facing the body. Maintain a slight bend in the knees if you are standing to take some pressure off the lower back. If you are seated keep your head and chest up.

Performance

Figure 6-27a

When performing the lift with dumbbells, begin the movement slowly by curling the weights (see Figure 6-26). Halfway through the lift twist the palms out, so that they face up. Keep your elbows close to the side of the body throughout the movement. Pause at the top for a second before lowering. Avoid any swinging motions with the back. Keeping the palms facing each other throughout the movement will place more work on the forearms. When using a barbell the action is the same with the obvious exception of rotating the palms (see Figure 6-27).

Figure 6-27b

Variations

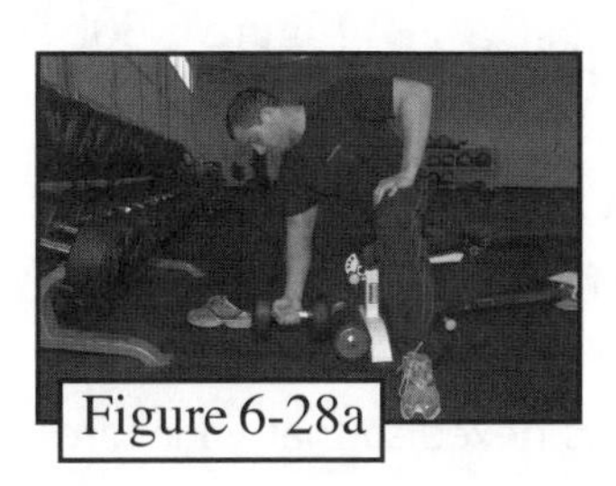
Figure 6-28a

A Concentration Curl is similar but the arms work independently (6-28). Sit at the edge of a bench and grab a dumbbell in one hand. Place the back of your elbow up against the inside of your thigh. Slowly curl the weight, keeping your palm facing up for better biceps activation. Hold for a second at the top before slowly reversing the movement. A cable can be used for variety. Pointing the thumbs up during the curling action works the forearms more. Another variation is the Preacher Curl (6-29). Sit on a preacher curl bench; place the back of your arms against the pad. Grab hold of an E-Z curl bar. Begin by slowly curling the weight upwards. Hold at

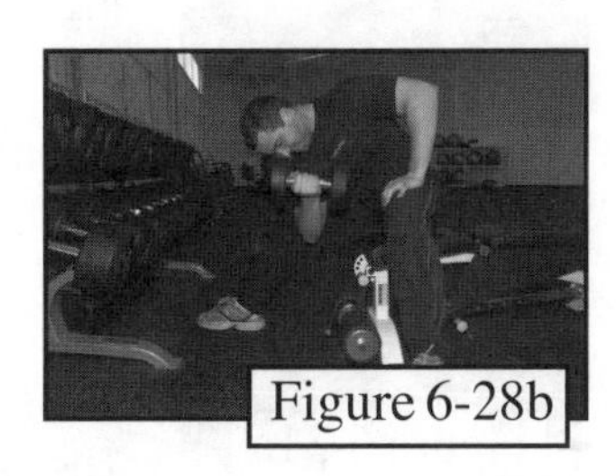
Figure 6-28b

the top for a second but do not lose tension by allowing it to rest, then slowly reverse the movement.

Figure 6-29

Triceps

Pushdowns

A simple yet effective way to train the triceps muscle is by performing a standard pushdown. It is a great isolation exercise, but be careful to use full range of motion to ensure that strength is improved through full range of motion and flexibility is maintained.

Figure 6-30a

Figure 6-30b

Position

The exercise can be performed using a cable pulley station or a triceps pushdown machine. When using a cable pulley system it is done by standing facing the cable pulley station (see Figure 6-30). You then grab a short bar with an overhand grip, palms facing down and elbows flexed so that your forearm meets your biceps. Slightly bend your knees and maintain a natural arch of the lower back, keeping your chest up. The arms should be up against the sides of the body during the movement and elbows will act only as a hinge. When using a triceps pushdown

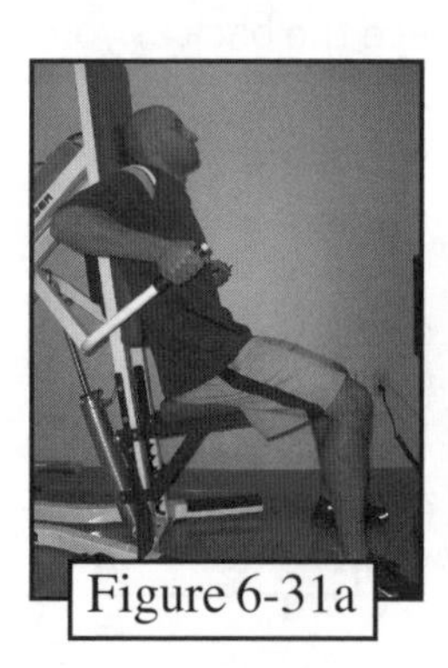
Figure 6-31a

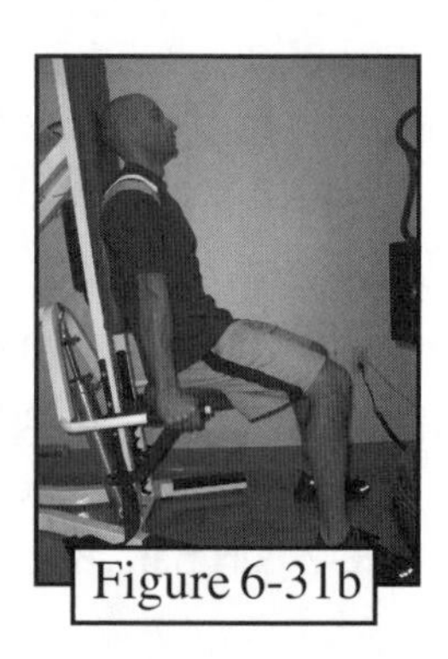
Figure 6-31b

machine, adjust the seat so that your arms are in a comfortably flexed position without shoulder elevation (see Figure 6-31).

Performance

For the cable pushdown, start by extending the arms downward, squeezing the triceps hard at the bottom of the movement. Slowly allow the bar to return to the starting position. A mistake commonly made is stopping the bar when the elbows reach a 90-degree angle. Don't short-change the triceps by doing this. Allow for a full range of motion. You can change emphasis on different parts of the triceps by using different handles. You can also take an underhand grip and change the feel of the exercise. For the triceps pushdown simply extend the elbows to full extension and then return the handles to the starting position.

Variations

Figure 6-32a

This variation is called a skull crusher, a nose breaker, and a number of other names indicating the relative danger of the exercise. It can be performed in the seated or lying position. In the lying position you begin by lying supine on a flat bench (see Figure 6-32). Hold an E-Z curl bar with your arms extended at an angle slightly away from your head. Bend at the elbows bringing the bar down toward the back of your head, being careful not to clonk your noggin. Pause at the bottom, then extend your arms to return to the top. Focus on getting a good stretch on the triceps during the descent. Your elbows should be pointing up toward the ceiling the whole time.

Figure 6-32b

Figure 6-33a

For a different feel, try dumbbells. When performing the exercise in the seated position start by overlapping your hands, resting one side of a dumbbell on the palms of your hands and letting the rest of the dumbbell hang through your hands (see Figure 6-33). Sit on a seated bench and hold the dumbbell over your head, then bending the elbows lower the dumbbell slowly down the back and return it to the starting position.

Figure 6-33b

Forearms

The forearms are one of the most neglected body parts. The wrist curl works the muscles that flex the wrist, while wrist extension improves wrist extension strength.

Figure 6-34a

Wrist Curls

Place the forearms at the edge of a bench holding a dumbbell in one hand (see Figure 6-34). Allow the wrist to extend over the edge of the bench. Start by slowly curling the dumbbell up until the wrist is fully flexed. Hold the top position for a second before slowly lowering the weight. A barbell can be used to train both forearms at the same time.

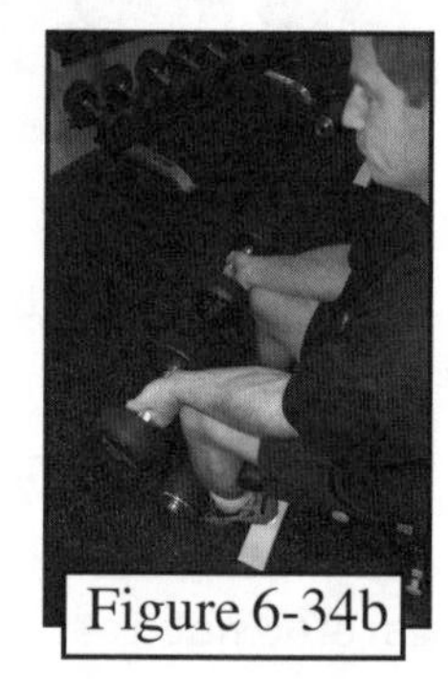
Figure 6-34b

Wrist Extensions

This is the reverse action of the wrist curl that trains the extensor muscle of the wrist. Place the forearms at the edge of the bench. Begin holding a dumbbell in one hand with the palms facing down. Slowly extend the wrist to the top position squeezing at the top. Slowly release back down. Both forearms can be trained by utilizing a bar (see Figure 6-35).

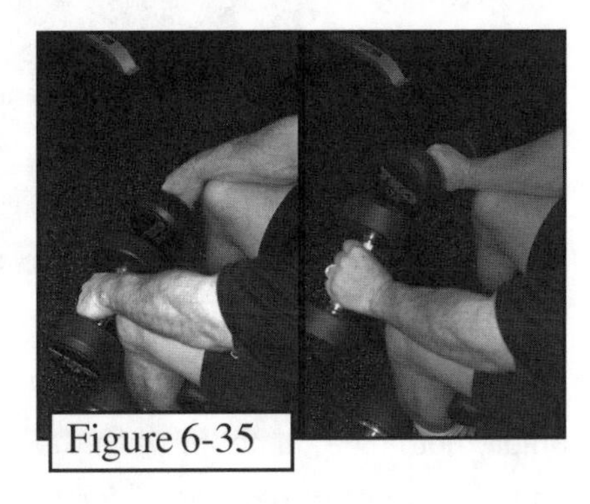
Figure 6-35

Rotator Cuff – Shoulder Joint

Internal/External Rotations

The shoulder capsule is often neglected in training. Considering the velocity of rotation that the shoulder undergoes during throwing, tennis, or other ballistic activities, this is an area that should be targeted, especially if there is history of injury. The major rotator cuff movements are internal and external rotation (twisting the arm inward and outward). For maximum benefit, these should be performed in multiple planes.

Figure 6-36

Figure 6-37

Figure 6-38

Although people attempt to target these muscles, the movements they use are often incorrect and the resistance levels are inappropriate (for example holding a dumbbell with the arm flexed at 90° and twisting in and out provides resistance for the biceps but not enough for the rotator cuff muscles).

Figure 6-39

To achieve a well-conditioned shoulder capsule, you will need to perform internal and external rotation in 4 positions. Position 1 - the arm is flexed and tight to body. Position 2 – the arm is abducted 90° at the shoulder and the elbow is flexed at 90°. Position 3 – the arm is abducted at 90° with the arm extended at the elbow. Position 4 – the arm is fully extended straight overhead. For each movement, just the arm is rotated toward or away from the body.

Hips & Quads

Squats

Figure 6-40a

This exercise is considered the king of all exercises! The squat will train all the muscles of the lower body to some extent. This is one of the most technically challenging and

Figure 6-40b

demanding exercises you can do. It requires a general strength base before attempting it. Flexibility will also be an issue, particularly tight hamstrings and Achilles tendons. These issues must be addressed before attempting to squat with a bar.

Position

For beginners the proper movement pattern may be learned using body weighted exercises by sitting on a box or chair. Once technique has been mastered you can progress to bar squatting.

Place a bar across your traps holding it securely with your hands; keep your thumbs around the bar (see Figure 6-40). Keep your head up and your chest out throughout the lift. Place your feet slightly wider than shoulder width apart; point your toes out slightly. Take a deep breath and keep your abs tight to help stabilize your core.

Performance

Step backward out of the rack (not forward because it is difficult to back into the rack when fatigued at the end of your set). Begin by moving your hips and buttocks back (avoid bending the knees to initiate the movement). It is natural that you will lean forward slightly at the waist during the descent. Continue the descent until your thighs become parallel to the ground; typically considered a 90 degree angle at the knee. Do not bounce at the bottom position. Instead, pause for a moment, and after the initial drive from the bottom of the squat exhale forcefully as you ascend, pushing your heels through the ground while driving the hips forward.

Variations

Leg presses are a great substitute for individuals with back problems or other injuries that keep them from squatting and for individuals uncomfortable with the squat (see Figure 6-41). The quads, hips, and glutes get worked during this lift. There are many variations of the leg press from which you can choose. Properly adjust the machine so that it allows you to reach a 90-degree knee angle. Place your feet on the footplate. Recognize that most people believe that

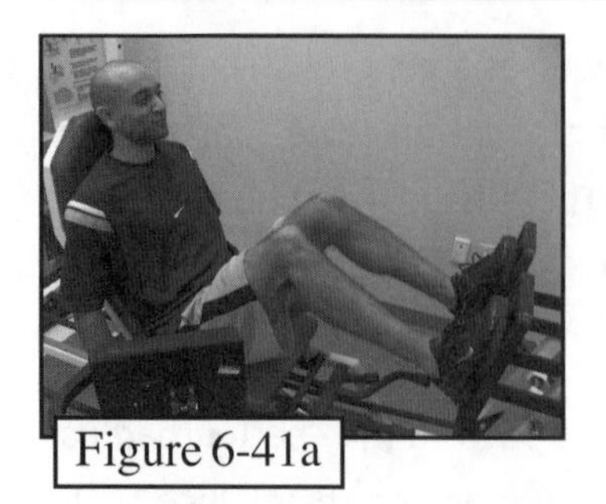
Figure 6-41a

the higher you place your feet on the plate the more the hamstrings and gluteus muscles will be emphasized and the lower the foot placement the more you target the quadriceps. Spacing between feet is also believed to be important; with a wider spacing activating the adductor muscles to a greater extent while keeping the feet closer is believed more effective on the quadriceps. However, it must be understood that all of these statements are purely anecdotal and controlled studies are necessary to confirm their authenticity. Begin flexing at the knees and lowering the footplate until you reach a 90-degree angle. Your hips and gluteals should be in contact with the seat padding the entire time and the lower back should have a slight arch. Avoid bouncing at the bottom. Don't let your knees go over your toes. Slowly raise the plate by extending your legs but do not forcefully lock your knees. Holding your breath while under a heavy weight is not advised as it may cause serious blood pressure conditions. Make sure to exhale as you lift.

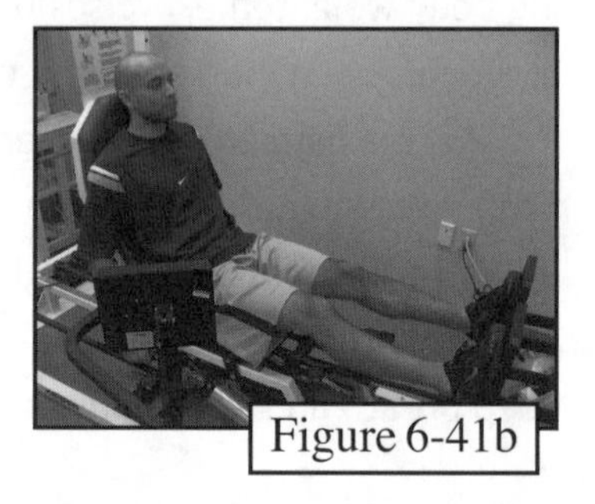
Figure 6-41b

The lunge is another great exercise for the hips, quads and lower body in general (see Figure 6-42). It can be more demanding skill-wise than the squats, so be mindful of your form. Stand upright with arms down at sides grabbing dumbbells or with the bar positioned on the back as demonstrated in squatting. As far as proper body position, the same holds true for the lunge as for the squat. Step forward about 3 feet or whatever distance is comfortable. Remember, that you do not have to walk like you are on a "tight rope", in fact, keep your legs shoulder width apart (this will improve your ability to balance the weight). The forward leg should bend down until the thigh is

Figure 6-42a

parallel with the ground and the rear leg knee should just skim the ground. Again, the lead knee should not track over the toes. Give a brief pause at the bottom and return to the starting position. This exercise can be done stationary or walking.

Figure 6-42b

Deadlift

This exercise demands extremely good technique and can be one of the most challenging and rewarding exercises in your arsenal (see Figure 6-43). While there is a heavy dose of lower back extensor strength necessary, the glutes, quadriceps and hamstrings will al lget activated at some point along this movement.

Position

The start position is a stance that is perpendicular to the bar, with the bar resting on the floor across the front of the shins.

You then bend at the waist, keeping the legs almost straight with about 10° of knee flexion (this is the modification). Stand with your feet about shoulder width apart holding the bar just wider than shoulder width with the palms facing backward (palms can be alternated as well). Keep the arms fully extended during the entire movement. Stick the chest out and pull up on the bar to reduce any slack in the legs and arms. The back should not be rounded; it should remain flat.

Figure 6-43

Performance

The key here is to keep the bar as close to the body as possible. If the bar travels too far away from the body or your form deteriorates, you may do considerable damage to your back! In general, the pulling motion starts from the floor and is complete at full lockout with shoulders pulled back and body completely erect. Start the motion with your hips down, chest out, and head up. Pull through the entire motion keeping the bar as close to body as possible. Move your hips up and in throughout the range of motion of the lift. Do not start by extending at the knee joint or the lower back.

Variation

The Straight Leg Deadlift is an alternative that places the stress on the lower back, glutes, and hamstrings, reducing the effects of the quadriceps (see Figure 6-44). The movement is the same, except that the legs are completely straight during the entire movement. To ease some of the lower back pressure, you may add a slight bend in the knees. This modified method is often called the Romanian Deadlift or simply the RDL.

Figure 6-44

Leg extension

This is an isolation movement that can really fire up those quads! While it is hard to perform this exercise without a machine, a clever person can do this same exercise with tubing and a chair.

Position

Sit on the machine making sure that you are comfortable by adjusting the seat to fit your body structure. Place the footpad directly over your lower shin area. Your knees should be adjacent with the machines axis of rotation otherwise known as the pivot point.

Performance

Slowly begin to lift the pad upward. Do not allow the hips to rise and glutes to come off the seat at any time. Gently lock out the knees at the top. Return to the bottom position in a slow and deliberate manner.

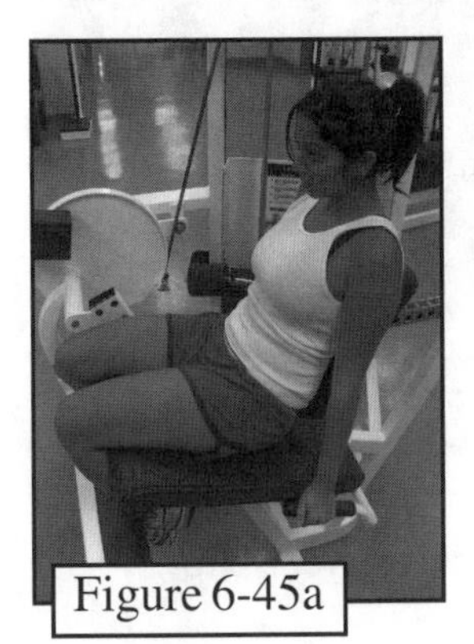

Figure 6-45a

Figure 6-45b

Hip Extensor, Flexor, Abduction, and Adduction

Perhaps the best way to isolate the individual hip activators is to use a Low Pulley Strap setup. The Low Pulley Strap can be added to a multi-station machine where there are pulleys along the ground. A simple belt will do, if no special strap is available, however, straps can be purchased at most fitness stores.

Figure 6-46

Position

The starting position depends on the desired action. One leg is strapped in while the other is used for support. The strapped leg should pull back against the resistance. For hip extension (glute isolation) face the machine. For hip flexion (psoas major) turn your back to the machine. And for adductor/abductor, stand perpendicular to the machine.

Performance

Figure 6-47

Pulling back on your leg while facing the machine works the hip extensors. Kicking forward with a straight leg, works the hip flexors. Standing beside the stack and pulling your leg out away from your body (like a jumping jack) will target the outer thigh (abductors). And to work the inner thigh (adductors), stand the opposite way pulling the same leg across your body.

Variations

Nearly every machine manufacturer now makes hip extensor, flexor, abductor and adductor machines as shown in Figures 6-49 through 6-52. The figures illustrate the use of these machines.

Figure 6-48

Figure 6-49

Figure 6-50
Figure 6-51

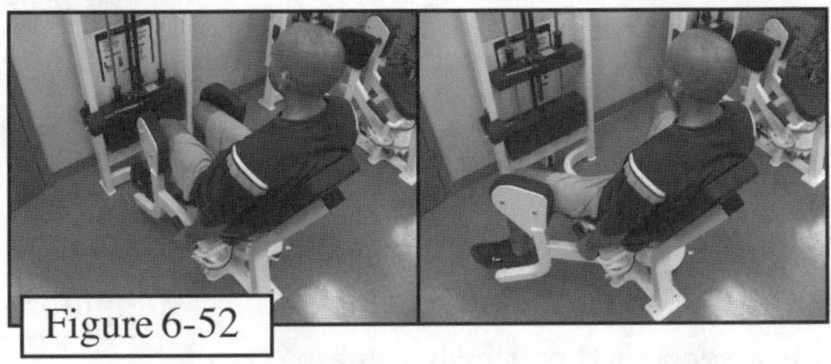
Figure 6-52

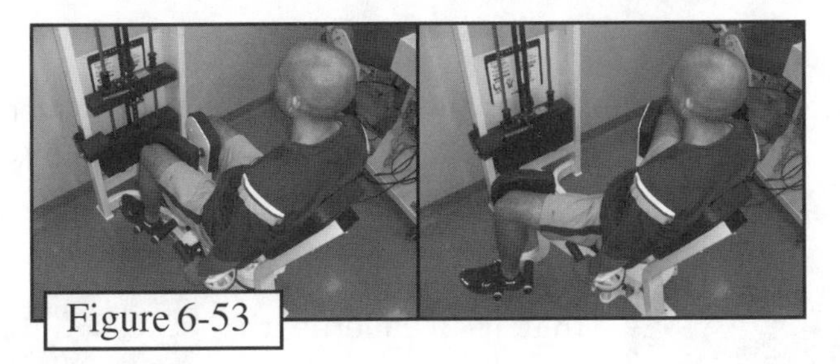
Figure 6-53

Hamstrings

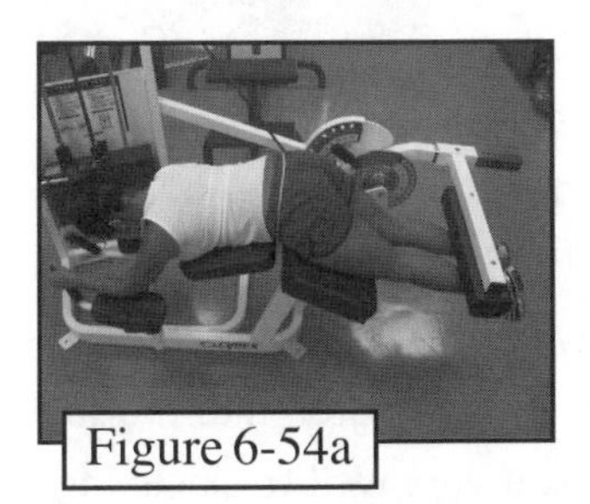
Figure 6-54a

Leg Curls

Training the hamstrings may not seem like many people's idea of fun; how- ever, balancing strenghth levels be- tween the quads and hams is extremely important for knee structure. Lying (see Figure 6-54 and standing (see Figure 6-55) leg curls will do just that.

Figure 6-54b

Figure 6-55a

Position

Adjust the footpad so it is over the Achilles tendon. Align your knees so that they are in line with the point, there is usually a dot marking this point. Lie prone or stand on the machine depending on the exercise. For the lying leg curl, keep your head down; looking forward can place strain on the cervical discs.

Figure 6-55b

Performance

Begin by lifting the pad slowly; do not allow the glutes to move away from or hips to come off the pad. Hold the movement at the top for a few seconds then slowly release.

Variation

The Seated Leg Curl adds a little variety and is often more comfortable on the lower back, however is not always found in all health clubs (see Figure 6-56). Adjust the pad so that it is underneath your calves. Place the thigh pad firmly against your quads. Start by flexing your knees so your lower leg moves toward your butt. Hold the top position for a moment, then slowly release by extending the knees. Maintain a slow piston-like motion throughout the lift. This exercise lends itself very well to single leg-work. Another variation is lifting with both legs and alternating lowering with one. This will really get your hamys cooking!

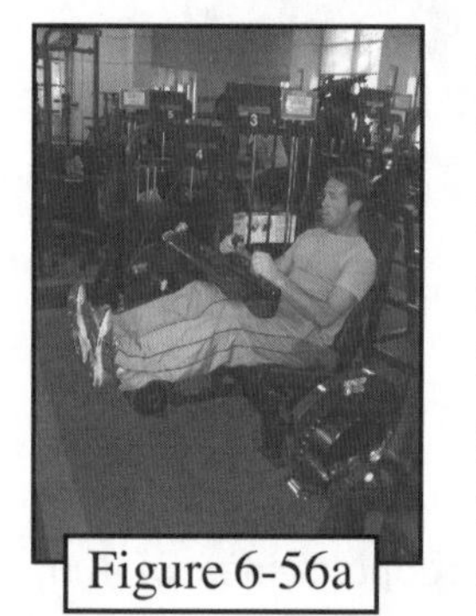
Figure 6-56a

Figure 6-56b

Calves and Lower Leg

Standing heel raise

From a performance standpoint, strength and power in the calves are very important. The standing heel raise will work both the larger gastrocnemius as well as the deeper, smaller, soleus. This exercise is often incorrectly called toe raises or calf raises.

Figure 6-57a

Position

Stand on the edge of a step or block. Only your toes and the balls of your feet should be in contact with the edge. Hold a pair of dumbbells at your sides (see Figure 6-57) or stand underneath a machine with shoulder pads (see Figure 6-58).

Figure 6-57b

Figure 6-58a

Performance

Slowly begin by pivoting upwards on your toes. Raise yourself as high as possible extending your feet; make sure to keep your legs straight. Contract your calves hard at the top for a few seconds and then come back down slowly. During the straight leg heel raise the gastrocnemius is the primary muscle being worked. This exercise can be done with a bar as well.

Figure 6-58b

Figure 6-59

Variation

Performing the seated heel raise primarily works the soleus muscle as it reduces some of the contribution of the bigger gastrocnemius. Sit on the machine and adjust the pad so that it's pressing against your quads. Place your toes and the balls of your feet on the footplate with your heels hanging off. Begin by pivoting on the toes and pushing them into the plate to raise the heels. Drive the pad upwards while strongly contracting the calves (see Figure 6-59). Hold at the top for a few seconds before lowering. Avoid any bouncing and ballistic movements. Maintain a smooth and steady motion throughout. The machines may also be designed where the plate moves down, away from the pad which is immobile (see Figure 6-60).

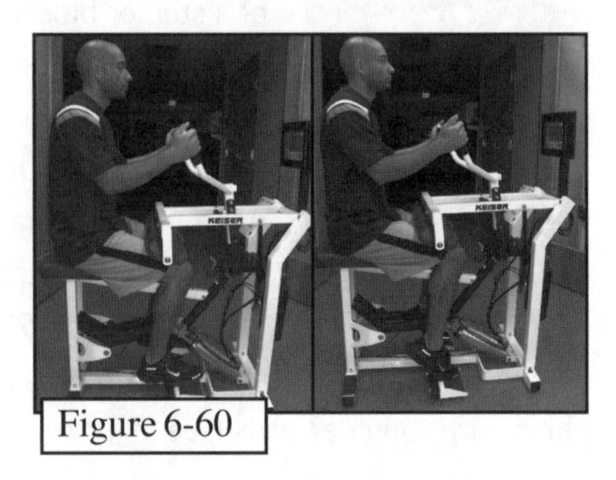

Figure 6-60

Toe raises

As the name implies, you will be raising your toes and working the much neglected anterior tibialis.

Figure 6-61a

Position

Stand on your heels at the edge of a high step. It should be high enough that when you point your toes down, they

Figure 6-61b

are off the ground. Your heels will act as the pivoting point (see Figure 6-61).

Performance

Slowly move your foot up and down. Squeeze hard at the top. Remember only your heel is in contact with the step. Another way to perform this exercise is to use a tube and pull your toes back against the tube (see Figure 6-62).

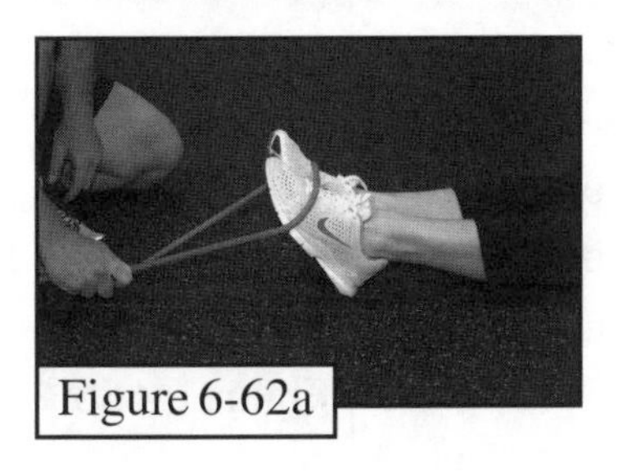
Figure 6-62a

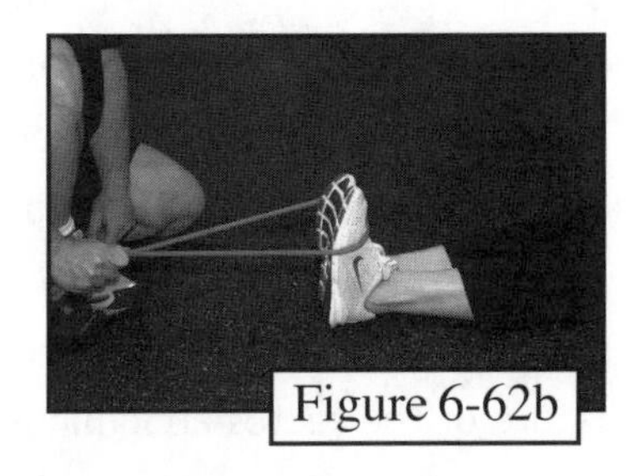
Figure 6-62b

Variation

Sit on a bench with a weight plate wrapped in a towel on top of your toes. Use your hands to stabilize the weight plate by holding the towel. Now raise your toes to lift the weight (see Figure 6-63). A second alternative is a specialized piece of equipment called a DARD (see figure 6-64) that is specifically designed to target the tibialis anterior.

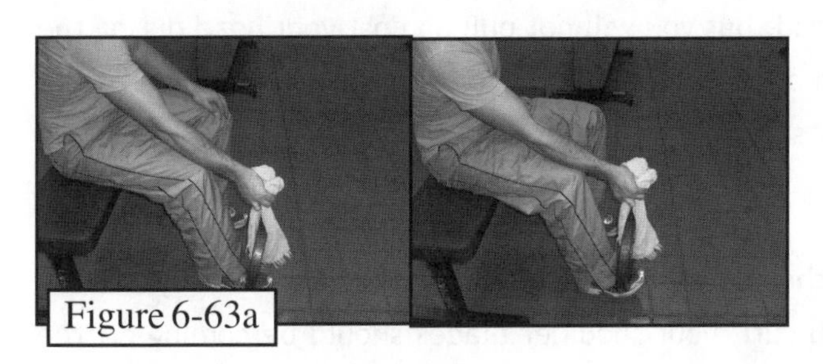
Figure 6-63a

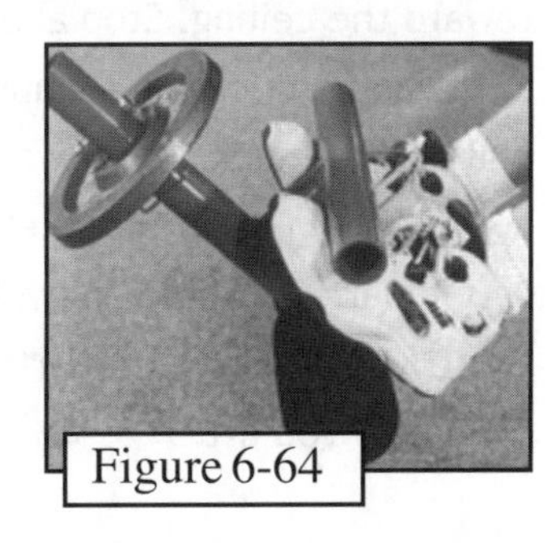
Figure 6-64

Abdominals

Floor crunch

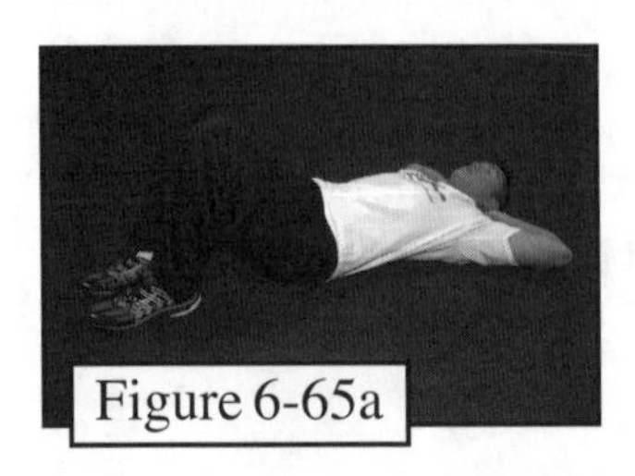
Figure 6-65a

What haven't we done in search for the washboard six-pack? From 6-minute abs to 6-second abs we have all been bombarded with plenty of gizmos and gadgets that provide more promises than results. Well, there's good news and bad news. First the bad news, if your body fat percentage is too high it will be impossible to see your abs under a layer of adipose tissue. Now for the good news, you can still strengthen and increase the musculature of the rectus abdominus (as well as the other abdominal muscles) with this simple exercise.

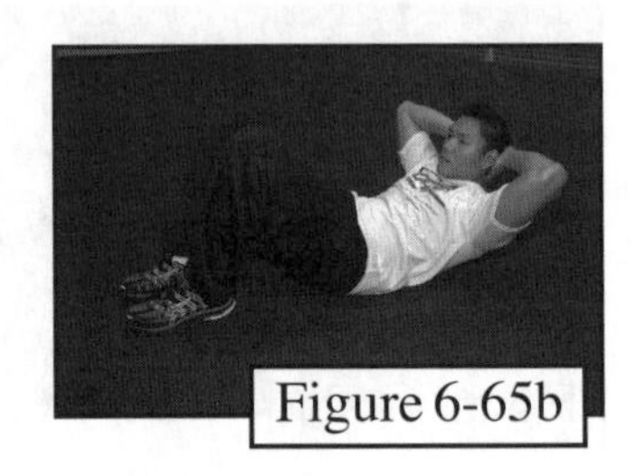
Figure 6-65b

Position

Lay down on your back with your knees bent. Place your hands behind your head; but you will not pull against your head during the movement. An alternate position is to leave your hands against the ground at your sides.

Performance

To begin the movement, slowly curl your upper body off the ground. As you curl, your shoulder blades should be coming off the floor. Think of raising one vertebra at a time. Keep your chin pointing toward the ceiling. Stop and hold at the top for a few seconds, then in the same deliberate manner lower back down. Make sure not to pull on your neck. The lower back should be pressed into the ground as you lift. In order for you to reap the true benefits of this exercise it is imperative that you avoid fast jerking motions. For added resistance you can have a partner apply downward resistance to your elbows as you lift.

Variations

Even though it is not possible to isolate the lower or upper abs, incorporating a variety of exercises breaks the monotony of routines. The Hip Raise is a tough exercise to perform and should not be done if you have a sore lower back (see Figure 6-66). Lie on your back, bend your knees and raise them up so they form a 90-degree angle. Place your arms down by your sides. Contract your abs lifting your butt off the ground and bring your knees toward your chest. Keep it slow and controlled. The range of motion is short but effective.

Figure 6-66a

Figure 6-66b

Another great exercise is the Twisting Crunch (see Figure 6-67). Assume a standard crunch position with knees bent and hands behind your head. Curl up as high as you can, then twist one elbow toward the opposite knee. As you twist, the focus is placed more on the obliques. Every time you curl up, twist to the opposite knee. Your goal is to curl up and twist as far as possible.

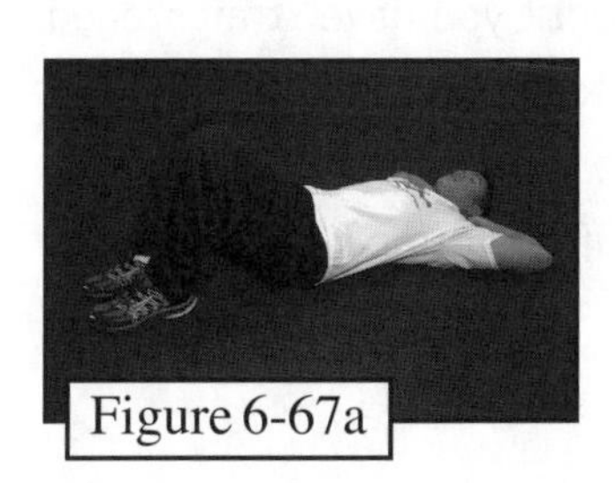
Figure 6-67a

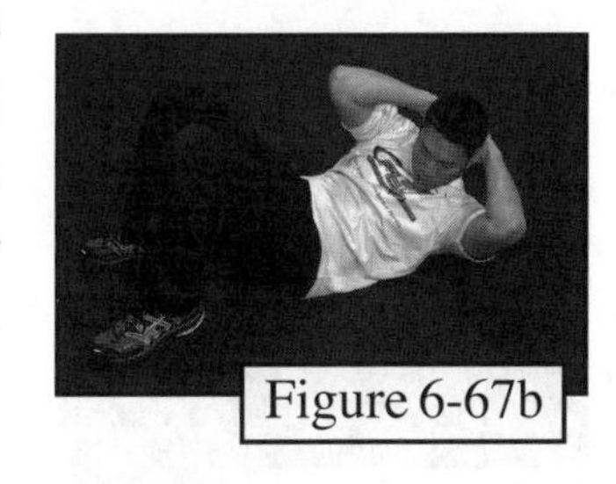
Figure 6-67b

Low back

Back extensions

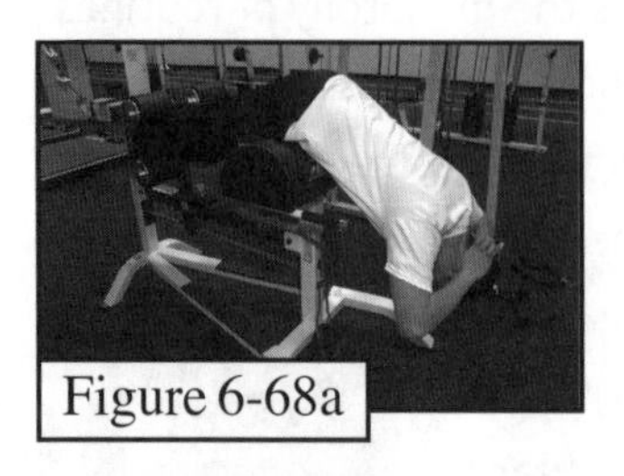
Figure 6-68a

The seated back extension will isolate the lower back muscle effectively if you have a machine to help with this. If not, the variation exercise listed below will certainly help.

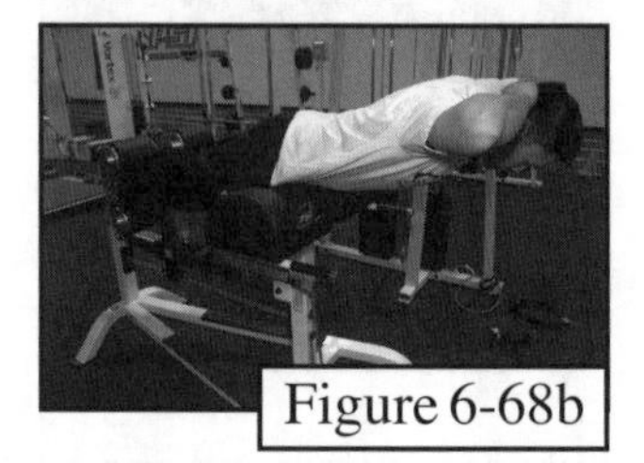
Figure 6-68b

Position

Start the exercise with your trunk flexed forward. Place the back pad directly on your upper back. Securely place your feet under the footpad. Keep your buttocks on the seat at all times.

Performance

Begin by extending at the hip joint until you have straightened your torso. Hold this extended position for a second. Release back down slowly. Keep in mind this exercise is extremely effective at strengthening the lower back, however if performed rapidly it can lead to injury of the area.

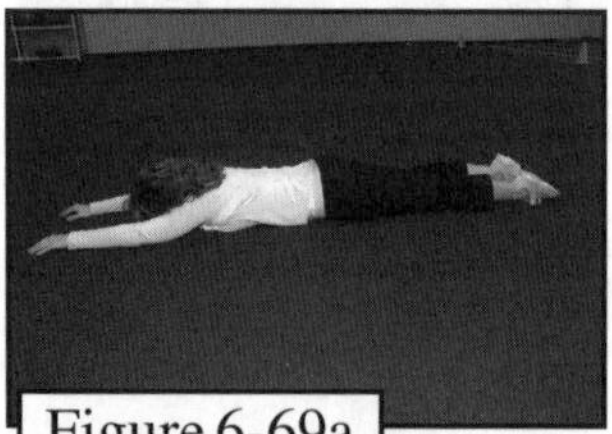

Variation

Figure 6-69a

The Superman is a great exercise for just about everyone. Of course, if you have a back injury, this is definitely one to avoid. Lie on the floor in a prone position. Extend both your arms and legs. You should look like superman in flight. Begin by raising both hands and legs off the ground. It is a short range of motion you will be working with,

Figure 6-69b

so keep your concentration of squeezing the low back muscles every inch. Hold at the top for a couple of seconds. Slowly lower back down; don't let your limbs come crashing down. Perform this exercise slowly to ensure its effectiveness.

Tubes and Med balls

Figure 6-70a

Chest pass

Have two individuals stand 3 to 5 yards apart facing each other. The first person holds a Medicine Ball at chest level. They will explosively pass the med ball toward the other person. The second person will catch the ball and rapidly pass it back. The passes should be performed as fast as possible. This drill can also be done alone facing a wall (Figures 6-71a & b).

Figure 6-71a Figure 6-71b

Overhead toss

Figure 6-72a

Begin holding a Medicine Ball with both hands at waist level. Quickly bring the arms up and back, then drive them forward releasing the ball as far as possible. Perform this exercise as rapidly as possible. Use only your arms to throw the ball.

Figure 6-72b

Figure 6-73a

Jump release

Holding a Medicine Ball at chest level, quickly dip down and jump up and toss the ball up as high as possible. Allow the ball to drop on to the ground, then repeat. This movement helps develop total body power.

Figure 6-73b

Figure 6-74a

Extended Row and Press

Two tubes will be used during the exercise. It will require two partners or ability to anchor the tubes to a piece of equipment. Stand between the two tubes facing either direction. Hold a tube in each hand. Extend arms out to the sides at chest level. Perform a simultaneous back row and chest press. Twist the hips and feet around, so that you end up in a lunge position. The movement is to be performed explosively.

Figure 6-74b

Figure 6-75a

Pull and Press

Attach two tubes to the same object or have a partner hold both tubes. Hold one end in each hand. Initiate movement with hip and knee rotation, similar to a baseball

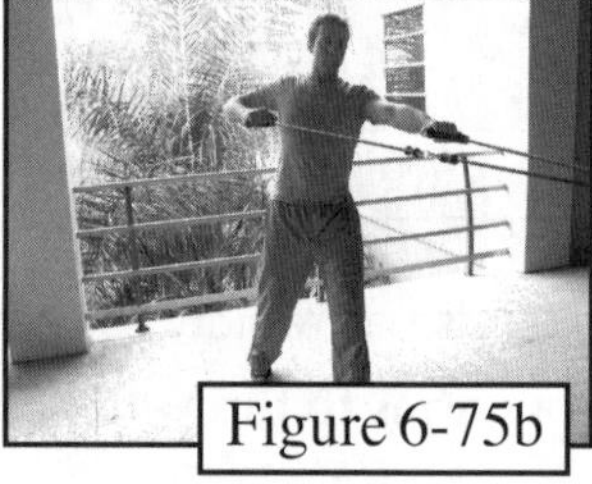
Figure 6-75b

swing. Pull with the far arm around the body and press straightforward with the near arm. Repeat movement, increasing speed with each repetition.

Figure 6-76a

Up downs

Anchor one end of a tube to the ground. Grab the other end with both hands facing the anchored end. Begin by bending at the waist with arms hanging down. Jump up as high as possible pulling upward on the tube. Make sure to extend up quickly at the waist, driving the hips forward and lifting the arms up as high as possible. If done correctly your toes should leave the ground during the jump. The tube will pull you down once you reach the top; quickly repeat the movement.

Figure 6-76b

Figure 6-77

Side twist

Two persons are required for this drill. Begin with each person holding one end of the tube with arms fully extended. The second person will hold his or her side of the tubing stationery while the first person rotates the torso away from the other one. Build speed as the repetitions increase.

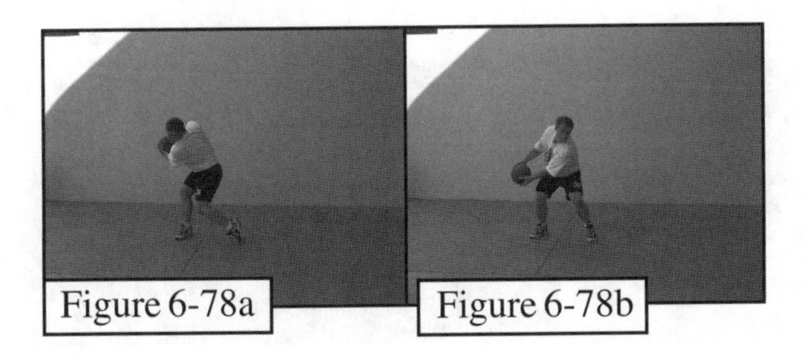
Figure 6-78a Figure 6-78b

Figure 6-78c Figure 6-78d

Figure 6-79

Side twist can also be perfomed by throwing a medicine ball against a wall (Figures 6-78a, b, c & d) or with a partner Figure (6-79).

Figure 6-80a

Circles

Hold a tube down low by the waist with both hands. Attach the other end down to the ground. Begin by pulling the tubes up to one side, rotate up and around in a circular motion. Increase the speed of movement after each rep .

Figure 6-80b

Axe Chops

This drill can be done with or without a partner. Hold a medicine ball at the waist level. Twist the torso up and away from the direction of the throw. Raise the arms up and back as far as possible over either shoulder. Use the lower body and torso to aggressively accelerate the ball diagonally and downward across the body. Release the ball directly into the ground toward a partner or a wall.

Figure 6-81

Twister

Sit on the ground with your hands in front of your body holding a medicine ball. Place your feet flat on the floor, and look straight ahead. Rotate from the waist and turn swiftly to one side as far as possible. Rapidly twist back from one side to the other. Keep the arms extended holding the med ball away from you at all times.

Figure 6-82

Power toss

Stand holding a medicine ball with both hands at waist level. Rapidly swing the ball a few times up and down between the legs to gain momentum. On your last swing, quickly dip down and then forcefully jump up tossing the ball straight up in the air.

Figure 6-83

One arm press toss

Stand with a staggered foot position. Hold a med ball with one hand up next to the neck and ear. Rotate back by bending at the hips, knees and ankles. Forcefully spin the body around and extend the arm forward pushing ball up and out as far as possible. The movement looks similar to a shot put without the spinning.

Figure 6-84

Chapter

7

Flexibility Training

Given the relationship between strength training and flexibility training and the misconceptions associated with this relationship, we have included this chapter in the text. It is not intended to be a comprehensive review of the topic. It is designed to address and clarify these misconceptions, explain the basic physiology behind flexibility training, show the differences among some commonly used stretching techniques and provide a series of stretches that have been shown to be effective in maintaining joint range of motion.

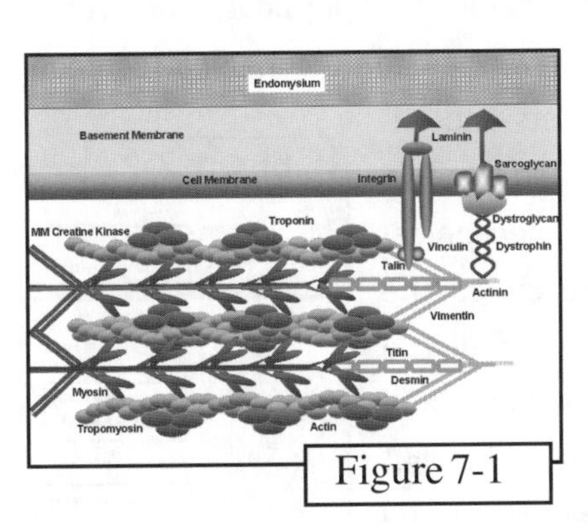

Figure 7-1

Flexibility Defined

Any attempt to provide an absolute definition of flexibility is affected by the structures that dictate this important physiological factor. We can define flexibility as the ability of a muscle to stretch. This would be dictated by the muscle's protein skeleton and the contractile proteins we described in Chapter 2. We have provided an illustration of these proteins (see Figure 7-1) with all their names just to show you how many "parts" there are inside a single muscle fiber (remember this is a muscle cell) that need to stretch when the muscle stretches. But talking about how much the parts of a muscle fiber can stretch is not enough. If you remember from Chapter 2 the muscle also has connective tissue both inside it (endomysium, perimysium and epimysium) and attaching it to the bones (tendons). These connective tissues also "stretch" contributing to a person's flexibility. Then we must also consider the things we examined in Chapter 3, the kind of joint, the "stretchability" of the ligaments and other structures that hold the joint together, and even the amount of stretch in the skin. All of these factors contribute to how flexible we are. Therefore we have decided on a much more "biomechanical" description of flexibility. We will define flexibility as the ability of a joint to move through its range of motion (ROM). Clearly every joint, due to its structure, has its own ROM. Also, different people will be able to move a specific joint through a greater ROM than others and will therefore be considered more "flexible".

The degree of stretch for these physical structures is the component of flexibility that we call the mechanical component. It is so important that scientists and clinicians have even named the two major elements of the mechanical component. They are called the series elastic (named for all the proteins that line up in a row) and the parallel elastic (named for all the proteins that line up side by side) components (see Figure 7-2).

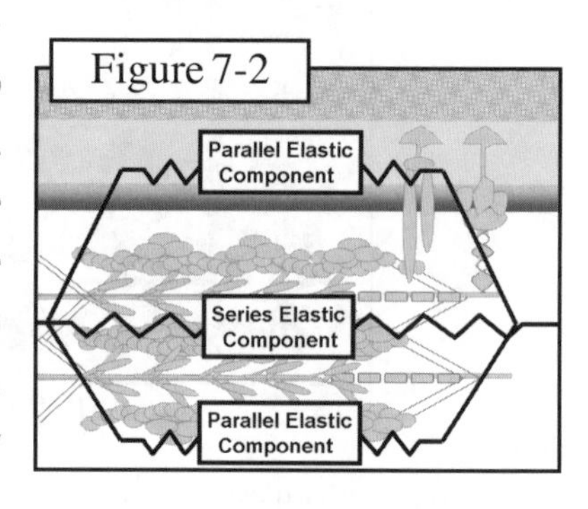

In addition to the mechanical components of flexibility, there are also neural (neurological) components. The protective mechanisms of the nervous system are called reflexes. If you close your eyes and move your arm, you know exactly where it is without looking, because your body has "receptors" or sensors that can "feel" the movement and tell you the arm's position. These receptors also provide a line of defense designed to prevent injury. Since this defense must happen quickly, it doesn't go through your brain. It happens by a simple loop of nerves that run from your muscle to your spinal cord, and back to your muscle. This is called a spinal reflex. We're all familiar with the simple knee jerk reflex: when the doctor taps your knee with a rubber mallet, you kick. This is the stretch reflex and is sensed by receptors called muscle spindles, which are buried within the muscle parallel to the fibers (see Figure 7-3). When your muscle is stretched quickly (also called ballistic), the spindles feel the stretch and send a message back to the muscle to contract, so that the stretch won't go too far and injure the muscle or joint.

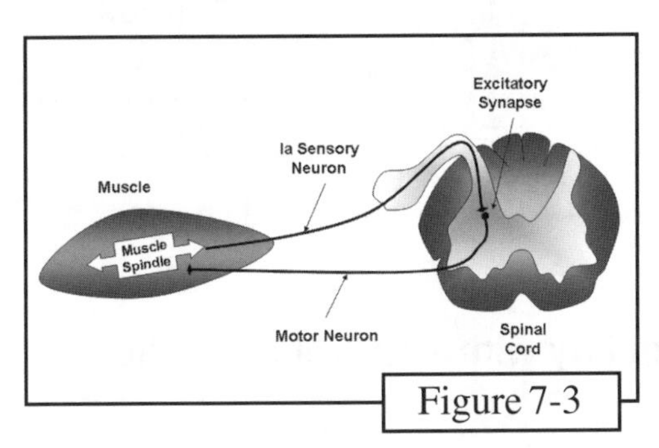

Figure 7-3

A second reflex is the inverse stretch reflex and is sensed by a completely different receptor located at the muscle tendon. This is called the Golgi Tendon Organ and it senses when the tendon is under tension (see Figure 7-4). Rather than causing the muscle to contract, this reflex causes it to relax since it sends a message to the motor nerve through a negative neuron which connects the two (called an inhibitory interneuron).

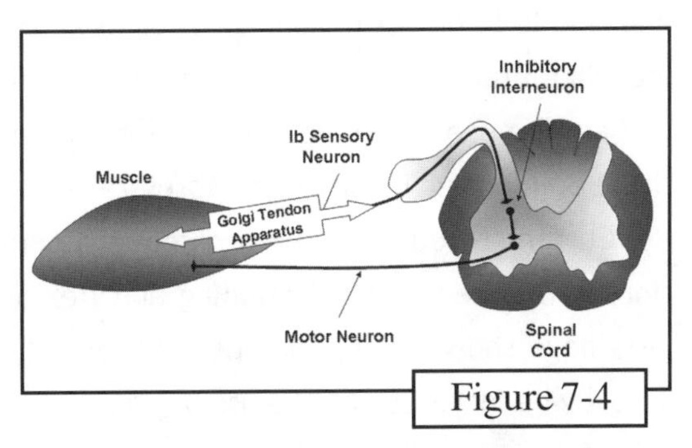

Figure 7-4

The third neurological pattern important in our discussion is called reciprocal inhibition. Simply stated this means that when a muscle contracts (the agonist) a message is sent to the motor nerve of the muscle on the other side of the joint (the antagonist) that tells it to relax. This prevents the antagonist from being injured, especially during high-speed explosive contractions of the agonist.

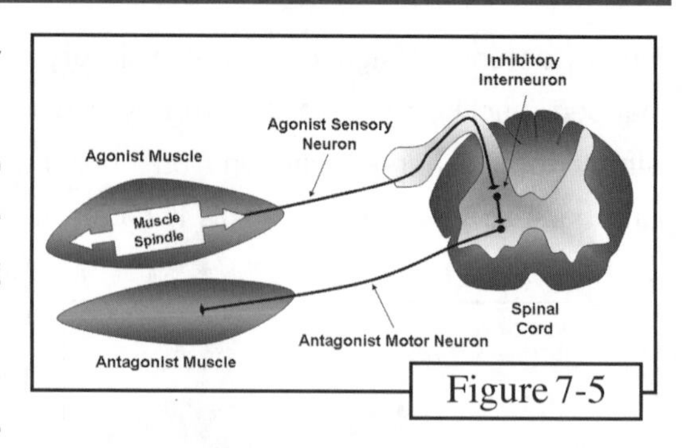

Figure 7-5

Thoughts about Flexibility without Stretching the Truth

The Myth of the Muscle Bound

Since we are talking about range of motion, let's discuss the best-known myth in weight training: becoming "muscle bound". The term itself conveys a picture of a person with so much muscle that he cannot scratch his own back. For years, this picture had been associated with weight training. Many coaches refused to weight train their athletes because they believed they would become inflexible, slow, and unable to perform. Many physicians avoided weight training during rehabilitation because they were afraid their patients would "bulk up" and be unable to make natural movements. The public echoed these opinions as if they were absolute truths carved in stone.

Current research, however, shows a completely different relationship between weight training and flexibility. Exercise physiologists have shown that flexibility cannot only be maintained, it can actually be increased by the use of proper weight training techniques using full range of motion exercises. While most studies indicate that there is no loss in flexibility due to resistance training, we ask the reader to remember one very obvious fact: when those biceps and forearms get bigger and bump into each other as you flex your arm, your arm stops. This is obviously a loss in range of motion. However, it has nothing to do with the physiological limits of the tissues, and everything to do with a simple law of physics: two objects cannot exist in the same place at the same time.

While it is true that incorrect lifting may cause a loss of flexibility, it is also true that correct lifting methods can actually increase flexibility. Research has shown that performing exercises through the full range of motion and concentrating on a slow eccentric movement can cause significant increases in the flexibility of the lifter. This is likely due to the increased tension put on the fibers during the lowering of a weight. Since studies examining the electrical activity of the muscle have shown that fewer fibers are activated during the eccentric (lengthening) movement, each fiber develops more tension, and therefore is stretched further during this portion of the lift.

Stretching Will Prevent Injury

There is a long-standing belief that stretching before performing an activity will reduce the potential for injury. While this is an attractive concept, there is little scientific or empirical data to support it. There are indications, however that persons who are more flexible will have lower levels of delayed onset muscle soreness (DOMS) following a high-intensity workout than those with lower levels of flexibility. So while data certainly support the use of a warm-up to increase the compliance of muscle and connective tissue before a workout, and the use of a regular stretching program to increase flexibility and reduce DOMS, the benefits of stretching before a workout or sporting event, unless that event is based on flexibility, are at best questionable.

Don't Stretch or You'll Ruin Your Performance

Recently there has been much scientific and empirical data indicating that stretching can have a negative effect on performance. However, these data need to be examined in light of other data showing that flexibility training can have a significant positive impact on performance, especially during explosive activities. It appears that the controversy needs to be addressed by asking a number of other questions. The first and most important is the concept of acute and chronic exercise. It appears from the current data that stretching immediately prior to a strength- or power-dominated sport or activity may negatively affect performance since it may reduce the amount of stored elastic energy that can be used during such endeavors. However, much of the data examining explosive performance after a longer period of flexibility training show the positive impact of flexibility on performance. Although it will take a number of controlled studies to confirm this statement, we feel that the current data support the positive impact of adding stretching to an overall fitness program; however, stretching immediately before a sport or event that requires your muscles to store and release elastic energy (See Chapter 2 on the stretch-shortening cycle) may negatively affect performance. What's the take home message? Get that body flexible well before that explosive event so that only a simple warm-up is necessary before performance.

The Physiology of Stretching

Very often we think of increases in flexibility as an almost spiritual experience, but the changes that occur with flexibility training are as real and tangible as those that occur with resistance training. Just as the muscle can grow by increasing its cross-sectional area when it is asked to lift more weight, it can also grow by increasing its length when it is stretched. In fact, we know that a muscle will actually add sarcomeres.

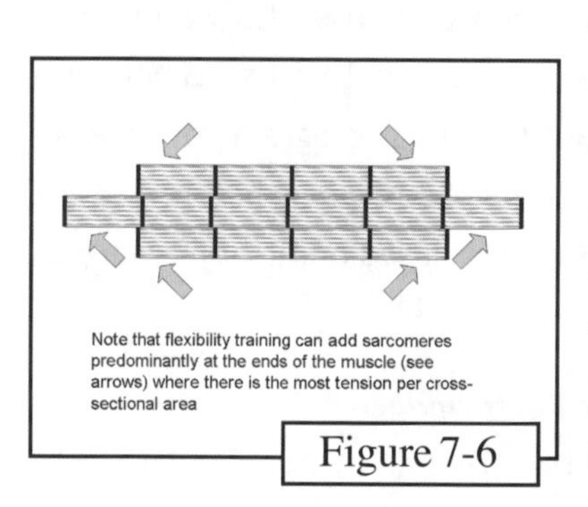

Note that flexibility training can add sarcomeres predominantly at the ends of the muscle (see arrows) where there is the most tension per cross-sectional area

Figure 7-6

In addition to adding sarcomeres to the muscle, stretching may also increase the length and compliancy (stretchability) of the connective tissues within a muscle, connecting the muscle to the bone (tendon) and connecting bones to bones (ligaments). All of these physical changes increase the length of ROM at the joint and therefore increase flexibility.

Stretching Techniques

While there is a vast array of stretching techniques available, they may be classified under three basic categories: static stretches, dynamic stretches, and proprioceptive neuromuscular facilitation (PNF) stretches. Static stretches are those where a body segment is placed in a position which causes a muscle to be put under tension and subsequently stretched. That stretch is then held for a period of time without any overt movement. Dynamic stretches are stretches where movement is used to stretch the muscle. If these stretches are done at increased movement speeds they are often called ballistic stretches. Finally PNF stretches are stretches where the reflexes we described earlier are used to make the stretch more effective and easier to perform.

There are potential dangers associated with dynamic stretching, especially if it is ballistic. Additionally, weight-training already constitutes a dynamic stretching method when performed through the full ROM. Given the negative aspects of dynamic stretching, either static or PNF stretching is a more suitable choice. Since PNF stretching has been shown to be superior to static stretching, we will concentrate on PNF stretches in this chapter.

The PNF technique we have chosen to present is called active-assisted (AA) stretching. We have chosen this technique because it has been proven effective in both controlled scientific studies and clinical settings and because it can be performed, unlike many PNF techniques, without a partner. For the AA stretches we recommend between 5 and 10 repetitions, with each repetition being held for 2-3 seconds. For the AA stretches you will note that the first action is to use the muscle on the opposite side of the one you are targeting to stretch the muscle you are targeting. This is the "active" portion of the stretch. The next step is to use a rope, towel, or even your own arms if you can reach, to increase that stretch by pulling it a bit farther. This is the "assisted" portion of the stretch.

Below are descriptions of the AA and stretches we recommend for each body part.

Active Assisted Stretches

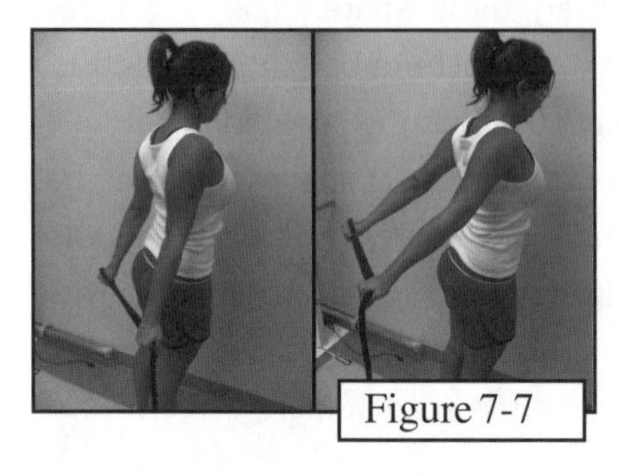
Figure 7-7

Anterior Deltoids, Biceps Brachii

Back Arm Press Stretch: (see Figure 7-7) Standing up straight, you will grasp the rope behind your back with both hands shoulder width apart. Keeping your arms straight, you will use the muscles of the upper back to lift your arms behind you and stretch the chest and arm muscles.

Triceps Brachii, Serratus Anterior

Back Scratch Stretch: Standing up straight with the end of a rope in your right hand, you will point your right elbow straight up. You will then reach behind your back and grasp the rope with your left hand. You will begin the stretch by reaching as far down your back as possible, then you will pull gently with your left hand to help stretch even farther.

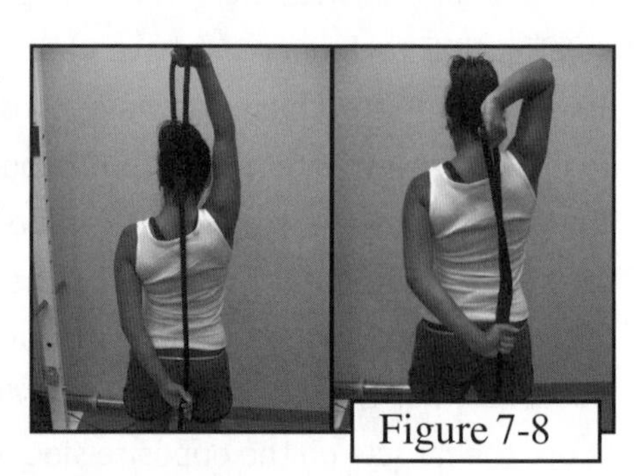
Figure 7-8

Anterior Deltoids, Pectoralis Major, Rectus Abdominus

Overhead Back Stretch: Standing up straight, you will extend your arms over your head while holding a rope with your hands slightly wider than shoulder width. You will start the movement by pressing

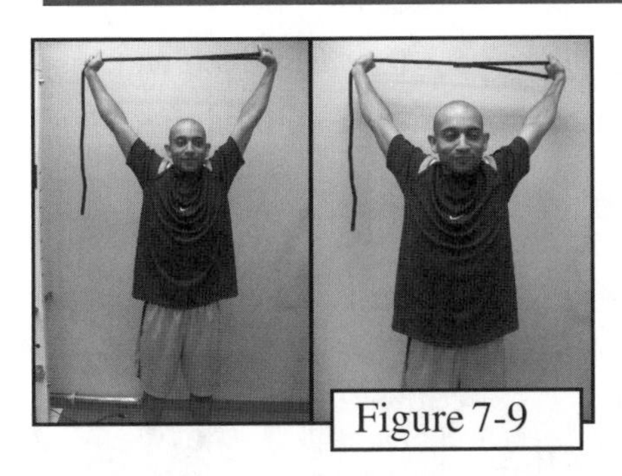
Figure 7-9

your arms back using the muscles of your upper back to stretch the front of the shoulders.

Latissimus Dorsi, Obliques, Erector Spinae

Overhead Side Stretch: Standing up straight, you will extend your arms over your head holding a rope with your hands slightly wider than your shoulders. Bend to the right using the muscles along the right side of your abdomen to stretch the muscles on the left side of your abdomen. You will pull on the rope with your right hand to assist yourself in stretching farther.

Figure 7-10

Posterior Deltoids, Rhomboids, Trapezius

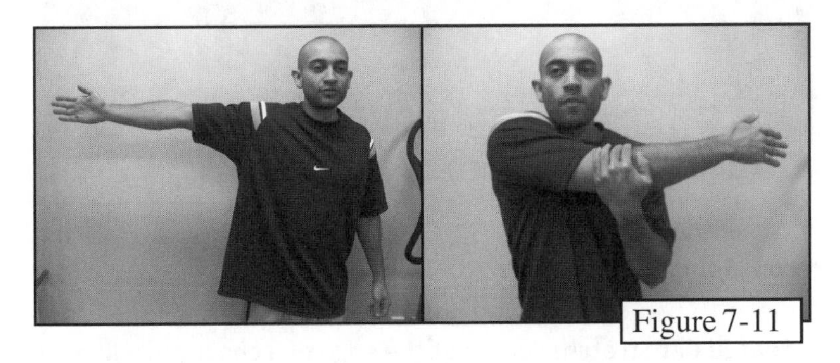
Figure 7-11

Cross Chest Stretch: This stretch may be performed with or without a rope for assistance. Standing up straight with or without a rope in your right hand, you will extend your right arm straight across your chest using your chest muscles. Using your left hand, you will then assist the stretch by pulling your arm or the rope to the left.

Rectus Abdominus, Obliques

Seated Overhead Trunk Twist: Sitting comfortably in a chair with your arms extended over your head, you will grasp the rope with both hands slightly wider than shoulder width. You will begin the stretch by slowly turning to the right using the muscles around your waistline.

Figure 7-12

Cross Leg Waist Rotator Stretch: Place your right leg over your left with the knee bent to about 90 degrees. Put your left elbow behind the knee. Rotate, using the elbow for leverage. Change sides and repeat the exercise.

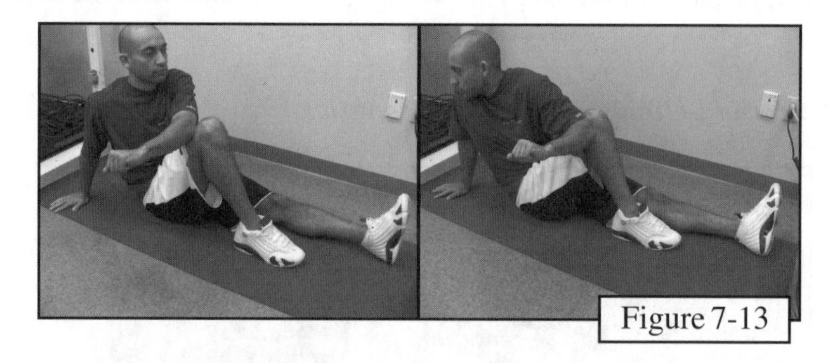

Figure 7-13

Erector Spinae, Rhomboids

Seated Cat Stretch: Seated at the edge of a chair, you will hold a rope with both hands and place both your feet in the middle of the rope. Keeping your feet close together and maintaining contact with

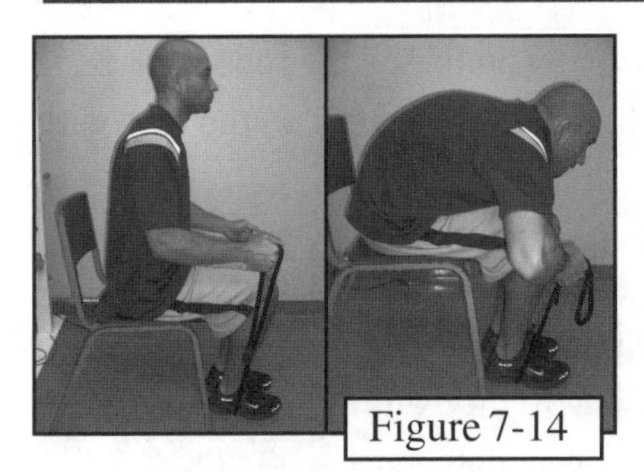
Figure 7-14

the ground, begin the stretch by using your abdominal muscles to stretch your back. When you have leaned as far forward as you can, assist the stretch by pulling on the rope with both hands.

Kneeing Cat Stretch: Get down on your hands and knees. Arch your back by trying to touch the back of your head to your buttocks. Then arch your back upward (chin toward thighs). Hold this position as you slowly sit back on your heels.

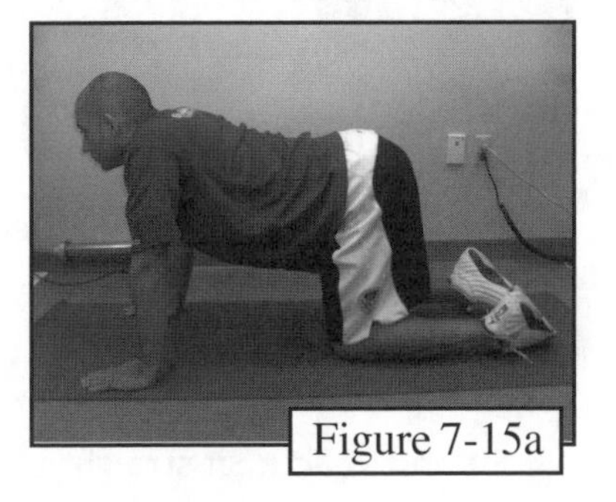
Figure 7-15a

Figure 7-15b

Hamstrings, Gastrocnemius, Soleus

Seated Hamstring/Calf Stretch: Seated at the edge of a chair, you will hold a rope with both hands and place your right foot in the middle of the rope. You will stretch your hamstring by extending your

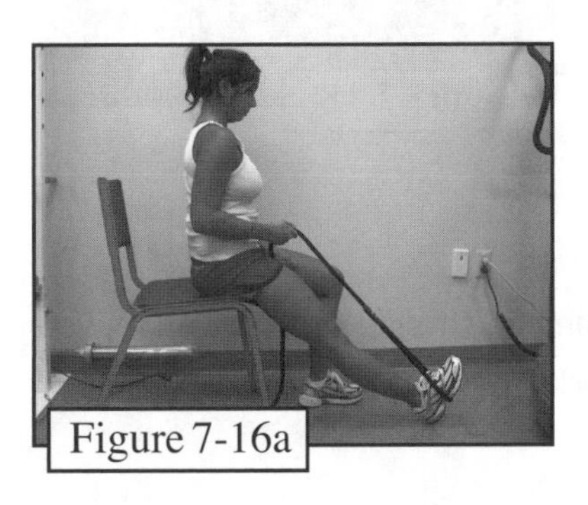
Figure 7-16a

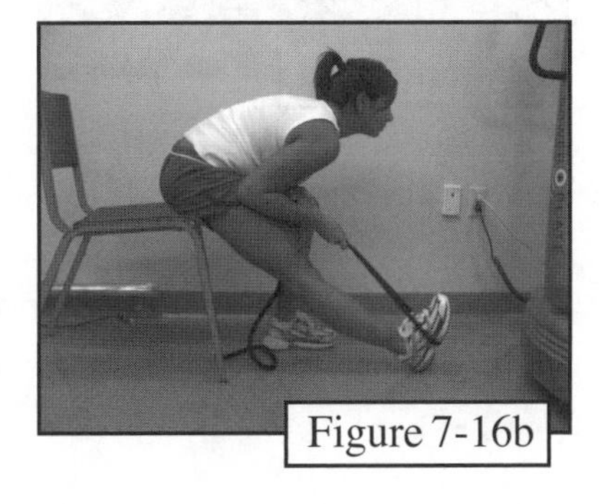
Figure 7-16b

right leg out in front of you and gently pulling on the rope. Your body will lean forward as you assist the stretch by pulling on the rope with both hands.

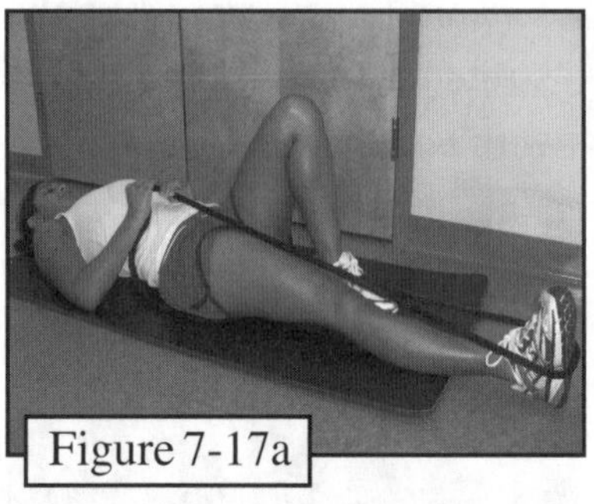
Figure 7-17a

Straight Leg Lift: Lying on your back with your left leg bent, you will extend your right foot straight out and place it in the middle of the rope. You will begin by raising your right leg as far as possible, and then assist yourself by pulling on the rope with both hands.

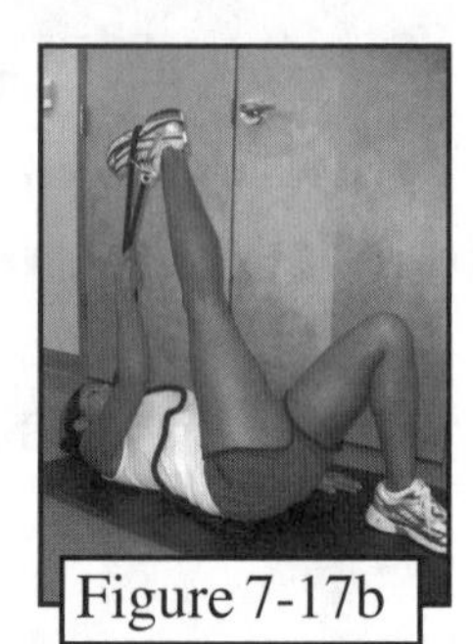
Figure 7-17b

Sit and Reach: Sit straight up on the floor with your legs straight out in front of you, the rope or towel crossing your insteps, and your hands at either end. Using your abdominals and hip flexors, lean as far forward as possible. Once you have reached your full range of motion assist yourself by pulling on the rope with both hands.

Figure 7-18a

Figure 7-18b

Quadriceps

Standing Thigh Stretch: Standing up straight behind a chair, you will hold onto the chair for support. Your right foot will be placed

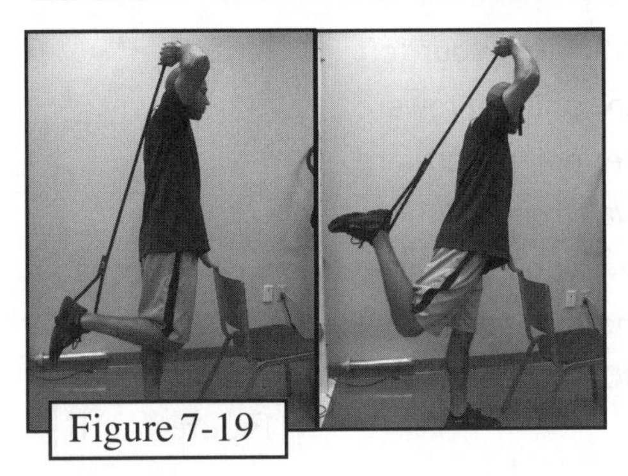
Figure 7-19

inside the loop of a rope. You will begin by bending your right leg behind you bringing your foot toward your buttocks. You will assist the stretch by pulling gently on the rope with your right hand.

Leg Adductors

Side Lunge Stretch: This stretch can also be performed with or without the use of a rope for assistance. Standing up straight behind a chair, you will support yourself by holding onto the chair. If using a rope, you will put your right foot inside the loop of the rope and grasp the other end of the rope with your left hand. You will point your right foot to the side and your left foot forward. Stretch by sliding your left foot out while bending your right knee over your right foot. You will assist the stretch by pulling outward and upward on the rope with you left hand or by pushing yourself further into the stretch using the chair for leverage.

Figure 7-20

Side Leg Stretch: Lying on your back with your right leg bent and foot on the floor, bend your left leg at the knee and bring it toward your chest. Place the loop of the rope or towel around the inside of your left ankle and grasp the end

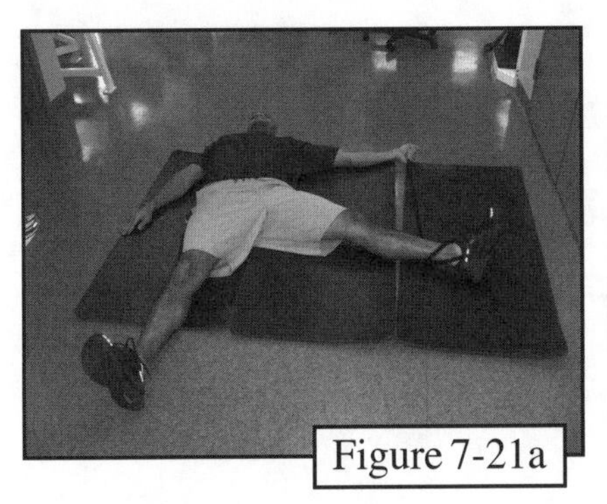
Figure 7-21a

with your left hand. Now straighten your left leg out to the side with the toe pointed toward the ceiling. Keeping your toes pointed toward the ceiling swing your foot away from your body in an arc as far as you can. When you have reached your full range of motion, gently pull on the rope to increase the ROM of the stretch. When finished switch sides.

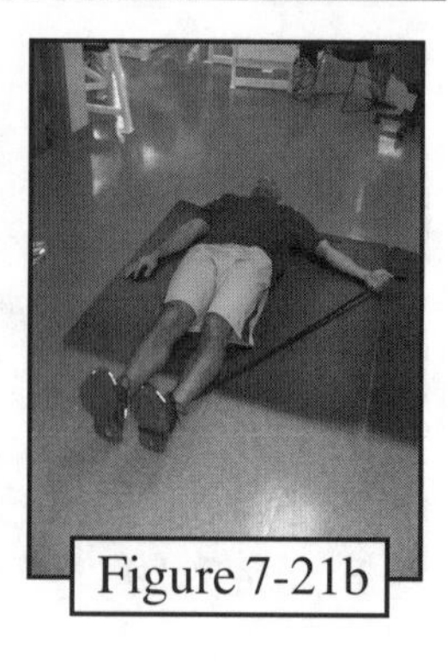

Figure 7-21b

Leg Abductors

Cross Leg Stretch: Lying on your back with both legs on the floor bend your left leg at the knee and bring it toward your chest. Place the rope or towel around the outside of your leg and grab the other end with your right hand. Using your adductor muscles move your leg as far across your body as possible trying not to roll. When you have reached your full range of motion, gently pull the rope across your body to increase the ROM of the stretch. When finished switch sides.

Figure 7-22

Gastrocnemius, Soleus

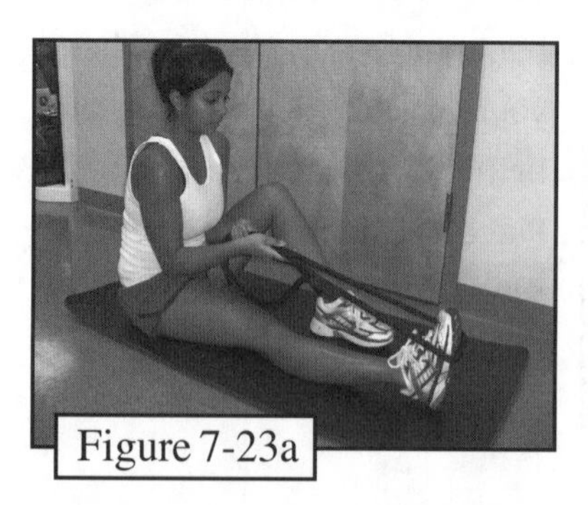

Figure 7-23a

Seated Calf: Sit straight up on the floor with one leg fully extended in front of you, the other leg bent with the foot on the floor, the rope or towel crossing your ball of the foot of extended leg, and

Figure 7-23b

your hands at either end of the rope. Using your tibialis anterior muscle, stretch your calves as far as possible. Once you have reached your full range of motion assist yourself by pulling on the rope with both hands. When you have finished switch legs.

Illiacus, Psoas

Sit upright, extend the left leg, flex the right leg, and bring it toward your chest. Grab the right ankle with your left hand, and block the leg with your right fore-

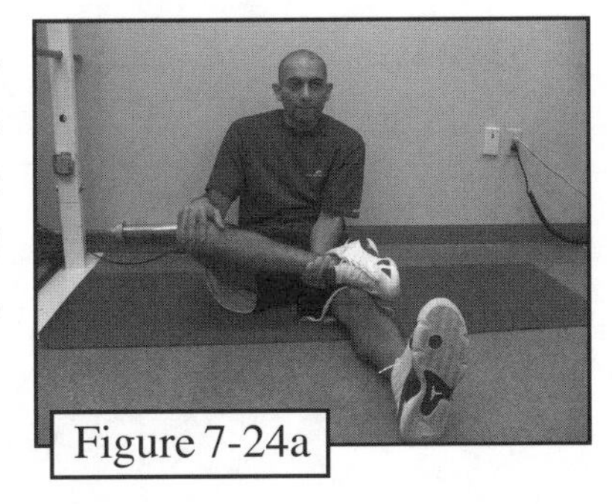
Figure 7-24a

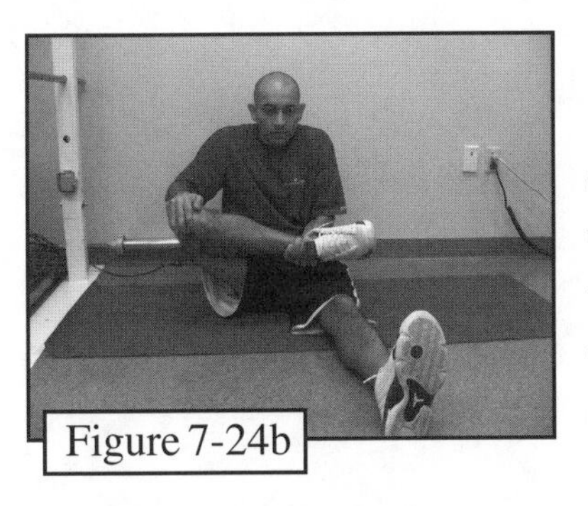
Figure 7-24b

arm and elbow. Pull the foot toward the left shoulder. Then use the hand on your knee to intensify the stretch. Change sides and repeat the exercise.

Groin and Hips

Sit with the knees bent and the soles of the feet touching.

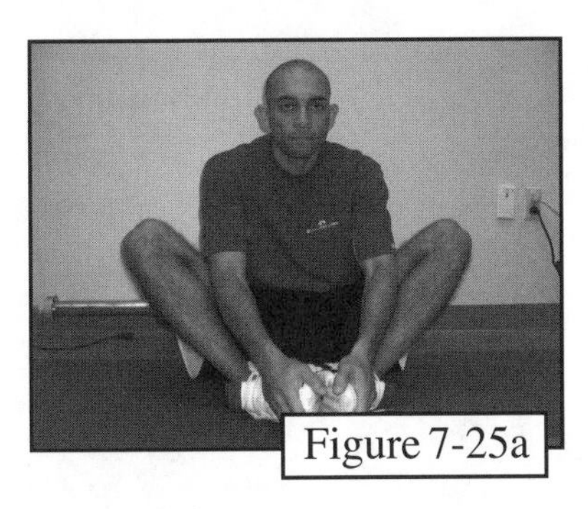
Figure 7-25a

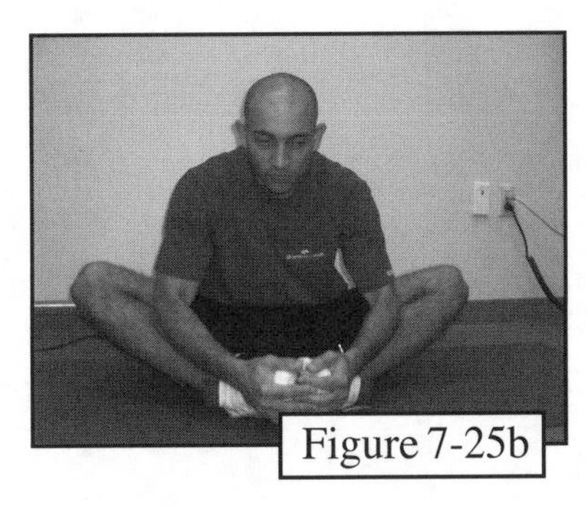
Figure 7-25b

Grasp put your feet together and attempt to bring your knees to the floor. Then assist the stretch by applying gentle pressure to the inner thigh, forcing the knees further toward the floor.

Chapter

8

Guidelines for Exercise Prescription

Why should we always perform 3 sets of 10 reps? Why should we count two on the concentric phase and three on the eccentric phase of the lift? Why should we isolate muscles so that their synergists (helpers... remember?) are not involved in the lift? These dogmas are the backbone of the traditional resistance training programs that have dominated weight training for more than 30 years. But are they really the best methods for lifting, or have we just been so conditioned by tradition that we're afraid to make changes?

What about some of the other questions that always circulate the gym? For example, are some exercises inherently better than others? Does the order in which you do the exercises matter? Does how much weight you lift really have any impact or should you just lift as much as you can all the time? Let's look at these and other questions that can have a direct affect on the design of your weight-training program.

Sets, Reps, Weight

At the heart of any training program are the individual exercises and the ability to arrange those exercises so that the muscles can be overloaded and have time to recover. Training protocols targeting different goals use very different patterns with respect to sets, reps and resistance. Recently, several respected research journals have published contrasting studies concerning the number of sets and reps that should be performed per exercise and per workout. This is now one of the most controversial topics in weight-training. The belief is that single sets are as effective as multiple sets in developing and maintaining strength. Although this concept appears to be supported in the literature, studies that support it vary in subject characteristics, sample size, exercise choice, and especially statistical power. You should realize that these studies are based on predictive statistics. This means that if not enough persons are included in the study, or if the people are very different in age and training status the two training programs may appear to produce similar effects when in reality they don't. We will base our opinion in this text on studies that have adjusted for these factors. Using these criteria, it appears that single sets may produce comparable improvements to multiple sets for beginning lifters or those currently at low fitness levels due to prolonged layoffs or injury. However, multiple sets seem necessary to provide a sufficient training stimulus for trained individuals. In addition, once a fitness level is reached, maintenance seems possible using a greatly reduced volume of exercise (see Figure 8-1).

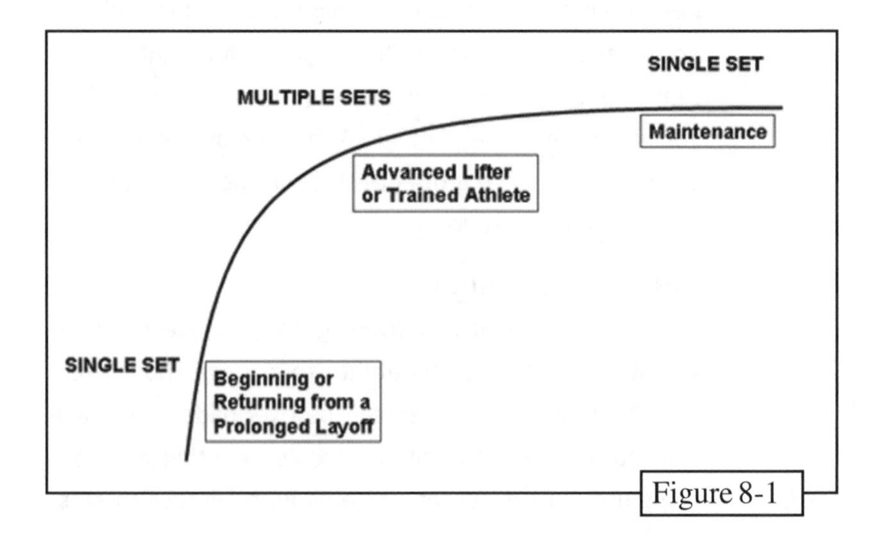

Figure 8-1

As we will see in the periodization chapter, even with trained lifters, the number of sets and reps should continually change depending on the level of overload required at any time point in the training cycle and the specific goal being targeted. Therefore, we feel that this debate, while interesting, is really an oversimplification with only limited importance in the context of modern periodization theory where changes in sets and reps (volume) are manipulated along with intensity (weight and speed) to provide periods of overload, recovery and improvement. This statement will be thoroughly explained in Chapter 9 when we examine periodization theory and application.

This is not to say that set/rep combinations have no place in the periodization scheme. In fact, quite the opposite is true. We will see that different set/rep combinations can be used to target strength, power, endurance or other performance variables in a muscle. But, we will also see that planning a pattern of change within specific set/rep protocols allows increasing and decreasing levels of overload and can prevent overtraining and maximize gains.

Set/Rep Target Zones: One of the basic concepts we have been alluding to throughout this chapter is the targeting of specific functional improvements such as strength, power and endurance by manipulating the load, repetition and set patterns of the workout. As described in Chapter 2, the degree of involvement of any muscle fiber and its pattern of adaptation are both dictated by how many repetitions, how many sets, and how much weight or speed you use. So whether you are trying to gain size, strength, power, speed, or a combination of these, you can control the general adaptation that will take place by setting up the appropriate protocol.

The general guidelines for specific set/rep/load patterns to target specific goals during single or multiple set exercises are presented in table 8-1

Table 8-1	Sets	Reps	Weight	Rest(s)
Muscular Endurance	1-3	15-25	Low	30-60
	2-5	10-15	Low	15-45
Muscular Strength	1-4	5-8	Heavy	60-180 90-210
Neurological	1-3	1-3	Very Heavy	180-300
Maximum	3-5	1	Maximal	180-420
Hypertrophy	1-4	8-12	Med/Heavy	60-120
Power	1-5	1-5	Medium	120-210

The following sections will explain why these set/rep/load patterns have been chosen for each of the specific goals listed.

Muscular Endurance: Before proceeding with this discussion, let's clarify some terms. Endurance is often considered to be synonymous with cardiovascular fitness. While this may be helpful in many discussions, the terms are not the same. Perhaps the most accurate definition of endurance is the ability to maintain a specific power output. We will be discussing muscular endurance in this section. This is the ability of a specific muscle or muscle group to maintain its power output. Obviously, this term operates on a sliding scale, so the sprinter trying to maintain speed in the 100m dash has one type of endurance and the marathoner trying to complete his or her race has another. For the sake of simplicity we have targeted short to moderate term muscular endurance in this discussion.

To increase this type of muscular endurance, you have two choices. You can either extend the set by completing more repetitions or have a shorter rest period between sets. The combination of both is probably best suited for most sports and general fitness programs. Generally when targeting endurance, a set should last at least 30 seconds and as long as two minutes. Any prolonged set will reduce creatine phosphate and increase lactic acid. Each of these may be limiting factors for completion of the set or sets. Having a longer rest or active rest will help remove or decrease the quantity of lactic acid built up and allow Creatine phosphate to be resynthesized (rebuilt) in the muscle (see Figure 8-2). Depending on your training goal, as you will see, it may be advantageous to train with high levels of lactic acid in the working muscle and bloodstream. Over time, training adaptations will improve the ability to tolerate and/or reduce the amount of lactic acid that is produced during each set. As this occurs the levels of localized muscular endurance will increase.

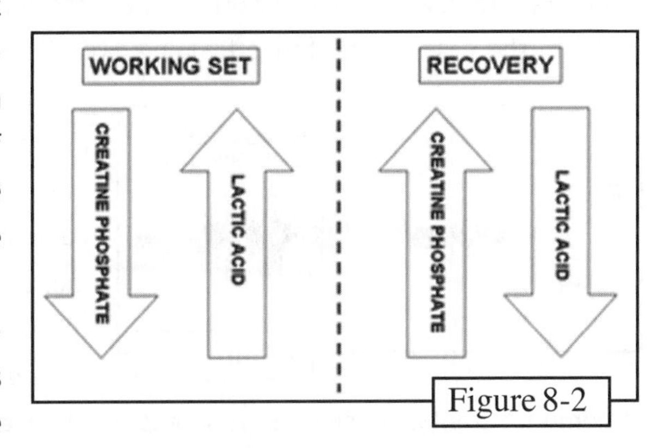

Figure 8-2

Muscular Strength: Everybody (well at least most guys) wants to have a big bench press, yet most people train using the wrong criteria for increasing strength. While strength is developed by using very heavy resistance during low repetition sets, it will not be effectively developed by "maxing out" or pyramiding all the time. Instead, a base needs to be built for true strength adaptation to take place and that is not accomplished by continuously "pounding away" at the muscles. Also, for true strength gains, your rest period should exceed 2 minutes (and preferably be 3 or 4 minutes) to allow proper recovery of your short burst fuel systems (creatine phosphate and ATP levels) and removal of the lactic acid built up during the previous set. Unlike endurance training, where the goal was lactate tolerance and maintenance of a rather low power output, the goal of this type of training is to increase the force-generating capacity of the muscle itself. Fatigue from this form of training primarily is from neurological failure, tissue hypoxia (lack of blood supply), and cellular disruption (damage).

Specific Strength/Neurological Strength: The term specific or neurological strength refers to the ability to call upon a specific number of muscle fibers to do the work - a.k.a. "recruitment" (see Figure 8-3). In the case of resistance training, we often think of it as the ability to lift maximally, however, it could also mean the ability to make controlled, finite movements. This type of training is used to refine strength for single rep maximum activity. First of all it should be clear that a large power output is not created during this type of training since load reduces velocity, although many might argue that this type of training is effective in increasing power since strength is one of the major factors dictating power. What this type of training requires is that the muscles increase their individual muscle fiber force-generating capacity and the nervous system's ability to stimulate (or call upon) the exact number of fibers to do the necessary work. Neurological evidence suggests that this process is learned, and therefore requires practice.

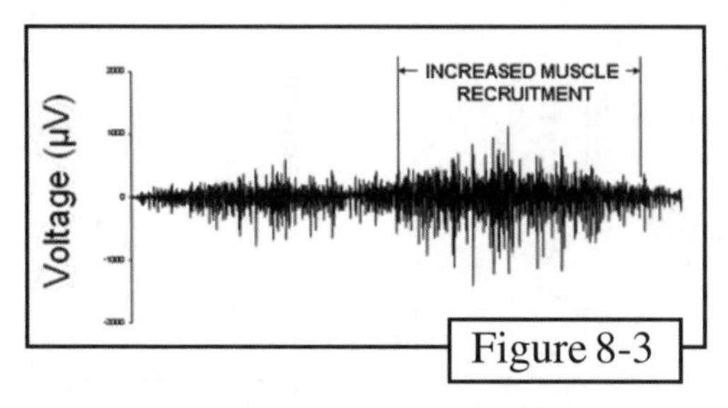

Figure 8-3

The concentration on single repetition strength has a number of shortcomings for most individuals. First, contrary to popular belief, this low rep method of training does not substantially increase fiber size compared to hypertrophy training. Second, although this type of training may serve the specific purpose of increasing absolute 1RM strength it has little benefit for most athletes or those of us who are lifting for fitness and health. Therefore, we do not recommend that any lifter attempt a max lift unless it is part of a well-supervised training program controlled by a coach experienced in this type of training. And if these criteria are met, one more should be included. The lifter and his coach or trainer should be able to provide tangible evidence that this training is absolutely necessary to meet the fitness, wellness and/or competitive goals of the individual. In short, if you are not a competitive power lifter, Olympic lifter or World's Strongest Man competitor, this type of training is completely unwarranted and the potential for injury far outweighs the potential benefit.

Maximum Lifting: This type of lifting is used to find a person's 1RM or single repetition maximum. In this way it is very similar to specific/neurological training. While it is a good method of finding your maximal muscle strength or force generating capacity, it is not a very good method of training. The major disadvantage in this type of lifting is that the adaptation is mostly neurological or recruitment based. This is advantageous for specifically increasing 1RM lifting such as a power lifter or Olympic lifter needs, but is not specific to most other applications. Furthermore, the rest time needed is so great that the workouts themselves have a very low work output (meaning not much actual lifting is performed) and require a very long time complete. We offer the same caution here that we did in the previous section. This is a very specific lifting technique and should be attempted only by experienced, highly trained lifters who are training for competitions involving maximal lifts (see Figure 8-4).

Maximal lifts should only be attempted by highly trained lifters.

Figure 8-4

Hypertrophy: Hypertrophy training is also called size building or bodybuilding. This protocol is used primarily by bodybuilders and recreational lifters. Hypertrophy training involves a moderate number of reps with moderate to heavy weight and average-length rest periods. This type of training falls between strength and endurance training. Research seems to indicate, the optimum number of reps are between 8 and 12. The optimal number of sets is between 1 and 4 although many elite body builders will drive this up into double figures. And the optimal rest time is one to two minutes. The idea behind this rep/set/recovery combination is to provide the greatest volume of work possible since volume seems to dictate size gains. If the load were too low and the repetitions were too high, the intensity would be limited and the individual would fatigue due to lactic acid and other waste product build-up before a maximum volume of work could be reached. On the other side of the coin, if the load is too high it will force the lifter to perform fewer repetitions that would also reduce the volume. Both research and practical experience have shown that the 8-12 repetition range allows the optimal balance between the weight lifted and the number of reps so that the maximal volume of work can be performed. The one to two minute recovery period between sets is sufficient to allow the muscle to perform at a level near the previous set, but only if more muscle fibers are called up (recruited) to help the already fatiguing fibers involved in the exercise. In this way a greater and greater volume of muscle is called up by the successive fatigue pattern created by each set, but recovery is sufficient to keep intensity high.

For the general, non sport-specific trainee, this is the most effective method of training for overall size development and body refinement. It should be noted that in general, all forms of resistance training will cause a muscle to increase in size and density, however, hypertrophy training helps you get there faster. You will also see that we recommend hypertrophy training when people are just beginning to lift or coming back from a long break. This increases the size of both the muscle and connective tissue and increases their capacity to handle the structural stresses associated with lifting. However, these cycles are a more conservative type of hypertrophy training that we call Tissue Adaptation Cycles, since they are designed to slowly increase the tensile strength of the muscle and connective tissue to prepare it for the stress of training.

Power and Explosive Lifting: This type of training is often confused with strength training since most people don't know the true definition of power. As you have already seen power is contingent upon two factors: force and velocity. Therefore, to develop power optimally, you need to move a relatively light-weight as fast as possible or attempt to accelerate a heavy weight as fast as possible (although the speed will be limited by the load). When training in this fashion, power decreases rapidly and energy stores are drastically reduced over several repetitions, therefore, it is recommended that only a few reps be performed per each set.

There is substantial research noting the benefits of explosive lifting and practical experience seems to support its positive effects. Often, this type of training has been inappropriately labeled as dangerous since the resistance is moved at high speeds and the inertia of the weights has the potential to damage the muscles and/or connective tissues. Perhaps a better way of looking at it is that preparation and correct equipment choices are imperative before power training is attempted. Prior to any power training, we suggest that the person work to hypertrophy both the muscle and connective tissue so that their structural strength is great enough to handle the ballistic nature of the lifting. Second, we suggest that lifting technique be carefully monitored especially when free-weight lifts are employed. In fact, free-weight power lifting should be used only by experienced, well-conditioned lifters. Third, hydraulic, rod, or pneumatic machines or other implements such as bands, tubes or medicine balls should be used by those of us who are not competitive lifters or athletes. The benefits are similar, if not better in some cases, and the risk is far lower. Finally, when lifting to develop explosive power the concentric phase should be performed as explosively as possible, but the eccentric phase should not. Lowering a weight very rapidly only encourages momentum, not power production, especially if the weight is "bounced" at the bottom of the lift. We recommend high-speed eccentrics be avoided since the potential for injury as you attempt to decelerate the bar during the eccentric contraction is extreme, and far outweighs the potential benefits involved.

One last point before we leave this section. We mentioned that power is the product of both speed and strength (force production). We also mentioned that it can be trained by lifting either light weights at high speeds or heavy weights at the highest speed possible. How do we choose which of these strategies is best? Once again the answer to the question is found in the goal of the training. For athletes like football players or power lifters we would recommend lifting at the load end of the load-velocity curve since the challenge they face is more dependent on moving a mass (another player or a heavy barbell) rather than moving at maximal speed. For an athlete like a tennis player or golfer, however, it is the speed at which their racket or club head moves that is most important; in which case our prescription would involve power training at the velocity (speed) end of the load/velocity curve (Figure 8-5). We call the targeting of specific areas of the load-velocity curve to meet specific needs "surfing the load-velocity curve". You will see practical examples in Chapter 10, which provides specific prescriptions for different individuals.

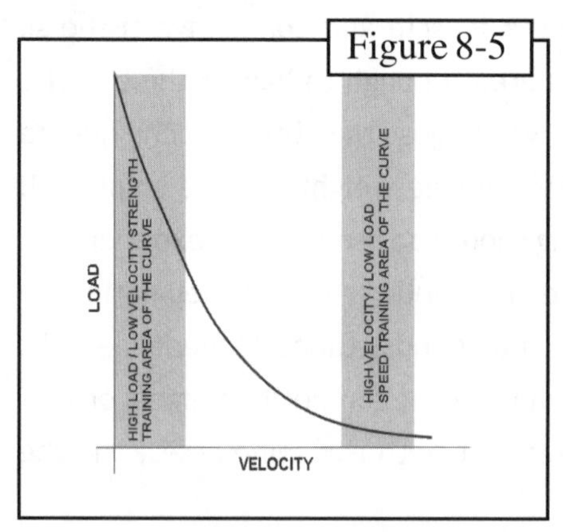

Figure 8-5

We would be remiss if we failed to mention that many coaches and trainers feel that the weight room is not the place to target power. They argue that no weight-training movement can truly simulate the explosive movements in sport and that these movements are the result of sequential firing of one muscle after another in a set pattern. This is called High-Intensity training. The practitioners who support it argue that the weight room is the place to develop strength and that power can be developed on the field, court or practice floor by practicing movements at high speeds using the muscle utilization sequences specific to the skill you want to train.

We have neither the egotism nor confidence to believe that we can settle this debate. What you will see as you examine our sample prescriptions is that we have adapted a middle ground where during the work phases of our periodization programs we use high-speed lifts employing lifting techniques that are appropriate to the lifter and offer the least potential for injury, and during our recovery phases we employ drills that translate these improvements into functional motor patterns.

Momentum

While momentum is important in running, throwing, jumping and other ballistic movements, gaining momentum by "rebounding" or "bouncing" the weight is only good if your goal is to "cheat" the weight up! Since a major goal of weight-training is to place your muscles under tension to help them grow, allowing other body parts to help in the lift reduces the effectiveness of the movement. In addition, the practice of using a body part as either a coil spring or rebounding surface to aid in the lift can be extremely dangerous and may even lead to muscle tears, ligament and tendon rupture, or fractured bone and cartilage (Figure 8-6). If your desire is to train

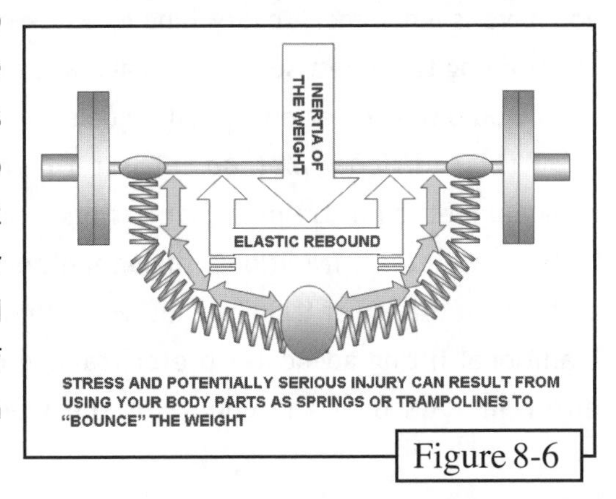

Figure 8-6

the elastic rebound of the muscles and tendons (stretch-shortening cycle), the safest method is the use of plyometric training which uses your own body weight to create stored energy.

Basic Training Theories

We cannot leave this chapter without examining the existing training methods that are currently dominating weight-training. There are several theories concerning the best way to increase size, strength, and power. We will cover a few of the major theories. But first, a caution. When an individual tells you that his theory is the correct one or that his method is the "best" or "only" method you should smile graciously and endure the flood of inaccuracies that will no doubt follow. As you will no doubt recognize from reading this book we have certain theories and training methods we prefer; but, it is our belief that each training method has its strengths and weaknesses. We also believe that different training methods target different goals and should therefore be chosen for use during one program or training cycle over another. In short, these different methods constitute different tools designed for specific purposes and a combination of training methodologies needs to be incorporated into any successful weight-training program.

You can't address the diverse goals of all weight-trainers using one training method any more than you can do all your household, automotive, or hobby projects using only one tool. And if you meet someone who says you can, remember the old saying, "if all you have is a hammer - everything looks like a nail". So let's look at our training tool chest so we can make a logical decision as to which tools would best meet our specific goals.

The Traditional Method: The term traditional refers to the common method of training that has been used for several decades to train athletes. Traditional lifting methods employ multiple sets and have a variety of training routines within a standard framework. Traditional lifting advocates prefer training different body parts on different days over the course of the week by grouping similar movements. They also advocate that lifts simulate sport-specific movements or everyday-life movements. This theory argues that a transfer effect will occur that links the lift to the specific skill being targeted. An example would be doing an overhead press to simulate "setting" a volleyball. Typically, the traditional method uses free-weights instead of machines for the exercise selection.

The High Intensity or HIT Method: A controversial yet effective method of training, HIT is not well understood by most lifters. First of all, the name is not very descriptive, since intensity can be increased by using more weights or moving at higher speeds. In theory, however, this method does have merit. It is predicated on performing the perfect repetition (as defined by HIT guidelines) with controlled momentum. Its underlying principle is that after an appropriate warm-up for the targeted joint and muscles, every set after that should go to momentary muscular failure (MMF). In other words, you should always go to the point where you are unable to perform an additional repetition. Most people believe that HIT training only uses machines and that you only perform one set of controlled contractions. In actuality, although repetitions are performed using approximately a 2-3 second concentric, 3-4 second eccentric pattern, multiple sets may be used and you do not have to use machines only. The major concept behind HIT training is that explosive lifts should not be used since all exercises must be performed in a controlled pattern to maximize muscle fiber recruitment and minimize the possibility of injury. The HIT practitioner would employ sport- or activity-specific speed development movements in drill performed outside of the weight room.

The Slow or Super-Slow Method: Often the "super-slow" method is confused with HIT training. The two are not the same. While there are several off-shoots, the main emphasis in super-slow training is that each single repetition takes between 20 (10s concentric, 10s eccentric) and 60 (30s concentric, 30s eccentric) seconds to complete. The idea behind this training is that the muscle being worked spends more time under tension, and therefore, receives a greater stimulus for growth. Although one study has supported the theory, the majority of the research, though limited, indicates that it is actually less effective than traditional lifting methods. In addition, other claims by practitioners indicating that it is superior to regular lifting programs for weight loss and that it can actually replace cardiovascular training are completely unsubstantiated. In effect, this method appears to be an overstatement of the slow single-set method originally proposed two or three decades ago. It has gained a following since performing the exercises in this way forces the muscle to contract with little blood flow (occlusion) and therefore, there is a significant amount of discomfort associated with it. In effect, this is a combination of the "no pain, no gain" theory and the opinion that muscular improvement is correlated with metabolite (waste product) build-up. Both of these theories, however, are incorrect.

The Bigger, Faster, Stronger Method: Essentially, the idea behind this methodology is that groups of athletes from kids to adults can learn through a progressive system how to combine regular resistance training with explosive training, plyometrics, and agilities to produce a substantial improvement in overall athletic performance. To some extent, all athletic training and conditioning programs use these training tools and incorporate several forms of training into their programming. Opponents of this training philosophy feel it is one-dimensional and fails to recognize that you cannot use a blanket type program for all athletes.

PACE Training: The acronym PACE stands for **P**rogrammed **A**erobic/Anaerobic Accommodating **C**ircuit **E**xercise although this name is somewhat ambiguous. PACE refers to the tempo at which you perform your workout. This method, where you keep a specific pace while limiting your set, reps, and rest time to a set time frame, is designed to provide a cardiovascular, as well as muscular endurance challenge. Typically a PACE routine has a 30s bout of work followed by a 30s active or passive rest period. Generally a true PACE routine uses push-pull movements with specifically designed hydraulic machines. However, other types of PACE classes are popping up in health clubs all over the world. Pace programming can also use a typical resistance training circuit with periods of light aerobic or even abdominal work between sets. When offered as an aerobics class, PACE training usually uses a circuit incorporating body bars, dumbbells, and tubing as forms of resistance. Since there is little experimental evidence to support this training method, it remains to be seen if it will produce superior results, especially in the area of weight loss where it has its greatest following.

Developing a Training Program

In this chapter we have presented a number of different training methods. This has been done to acquaint you with what's out there, but also to allow you to see and understand the proposed purposes, strengths and shortcomings of each method. It is our intention in the chapters that follow to explain how the different exercises we described in Chapter 6 and the methods described in this chapter can be incorporated into prescription training programs so that they meet specific goals and provide successful weight-training. In this way, we will explain how to develop weight-training programs for *everyone*!

Chapter

9

Periodization of Training

As you will recall from Chapter 1 there are two major concepts upon which this book is based. The first is *exercise specificity,* which we covered in Chapters 2 and 3 and which we will expand upon in the chapter on designing training programs (Chapter 10). The second concept is *periodization.*

Although there are a number of different ways to apply the theory of *periodization* to training, the underlying concept is quite simple. *Periodization* is a calendar of work and recovery designed to maximize improvements. None of us can work at maximal effort day in and day out without getting tired, yet many of us try to train that way. When we do, our energy systems, our muscles, and even our immune system fatigue, and we no longer make any improvements. In fact, in most cases we even lose some of the gains we have made. As you read this chapter we'd like you to keep one concept in mind. *Rest is a training tool.* Although your body may make some neurological improvements during the application of the training stimulus, the major structural improvements occur during recovery. It is during these recovery periods that the body regenerates its energy sources and changes its structures so it can make the specific adaptations dictated by the training stimulus. Without recovery periods the body will cease to improve, lose its gains and may even be injured. In addition, the immune system of the body is compromised every time we exercise and prolonged exercise without scheduled recovery periods can increase our susceptibility to contagious diseases. It is clear from both controlled studies and practical application that periodization produces superior results, reduces the incidence of overtraining and injury, and improves exercise efficiency and compliance when compared to standard progressive resistance training.

The Bases of Periodization Theory

Periodization theory finds its basis in the General Adaptation Syndrome (GAS) presented by Hans Hugo Selye, an endocrinologist, in 1936. He noted that when any organism is exposed to a *stress* it goes through a specific pattern or syndrome containing three stages (see Figure 9-1). The first two stages are inevitable. They are *alarm* and *resistance (*some may use the term *adaptation)*. The third stage occurs if the stress is not removed. This stage is *exhaustion*.

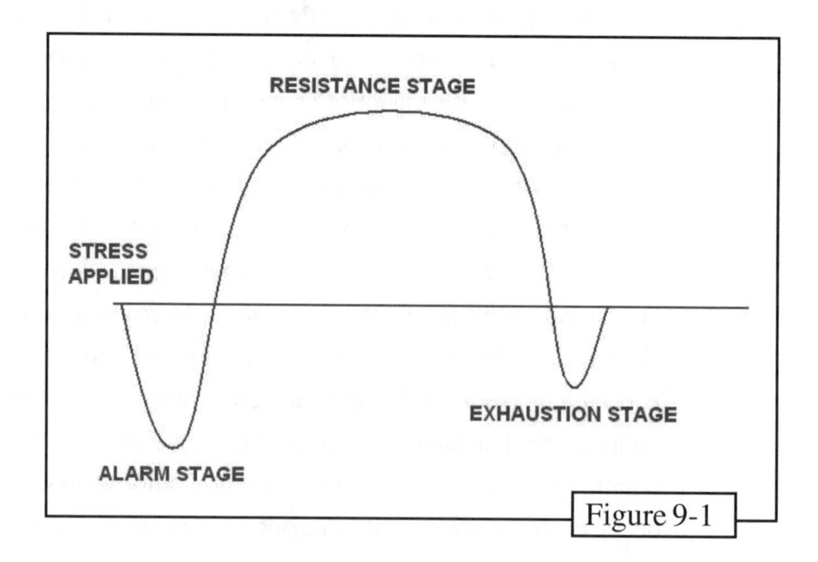

Figure 9-1

Let's look at each stage and see what Selye says about it. During the first stage, the *alarm stage*, the body's immune system is depressed. It reacts by increasing its *stress hormones* (like adrenaline, also known as epinephrine), which are released due to a typical *fight or flight* reaction to a perceived threat. As we said earlier, this happens during a single event or can last for a longer period of time if the stressor is applied for a prolonged period. While this theory has been applied to everything from stress management to cancer, our interest is in its application to resistance training. The next stage is the *adaptation* or *resistance* stage. Both terms have been used to describe this stage since it is a reaction to the stress. This reaction is designed to *resist* the stress by *adapting* the body to it. Once again this can be a short-term reaction, like calming down after you have been frightened, or a longer-term reaction, like when you gradually learned not to be afraid of the dark when you were a child (we hope!). The good thing about this *adaptation* stage is that the body doesn't just go back to normal; it becomes more resistant to the stress. When that *stress* is weight training, the body becomes stronger as it *adapts* to the *overload*. Selye's last stage is *exhaustion*. As we noted earlier this stage is not inevitable. It is the result of the stress being continued so that the body's functions are compromised to a level where they can no longer effectively adapt.

Although the concepts of work and recovery as they relate to strength training were discussed by the Eastern Europeans in the early part of the twentieth century, the application of this theory as it applies to Selye's principles was formally stated by exercise scientists like Matveyev and Vorobyev in the 1960s and 1970s. Their theories, originally applied to Olympic lifting, have lead to the general periodization curve that is the basis of the varied forms of periodization employed today. This curve is presented in Figure 9-2. As you can see, the curve is very similar to that presented by Selye. The first response to any exercise stimulus, and therefore the first portion of the curve, is *fatigue* (or *depletion*). This is similar to the *alarm* stage

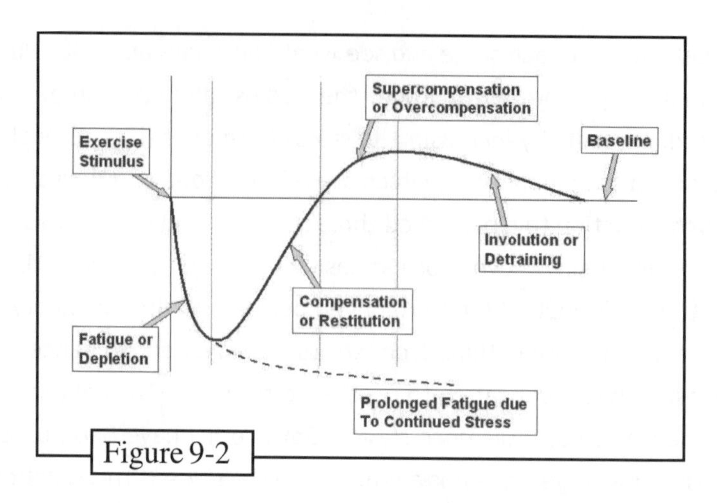

Figure 9-2

described by Selye. Remember exercise is an *outside demand* placed upon the body. As such, it will induce a *stress reaction.* This stress can be both a stimulus and a response. It is a stimulus because it can produce a physiological change in the body. It is a response because it is triggered by the stress of the exercise. So exercise makes us tired. Our systems (energy, tissue, and immune) all become somewhat depleted.

The second stage in the periodization curve is *compensation* or *restitution.* This is similar to the first half of Selye's *adaptation* or *resistance* stage where the body responds to the stress. In the case of exercise this stage requires a reduction in the level of stress so that the body's systems can have time to recover. This is the critical stage that many of us ignore, or even worse, refuse to acknowledge. We'll discuss this later in the sections on the practical application of periodization.

The next stage in the periodization curve is the *supercompensation* or *overcompensation* stage. This is like the second half of Selye's *adaptation* stage. If you recall, Selye's theory states that the body will not only respond to the stress but will respond by adapting to a level where it can handle that stress more efficiently in the future. In the *supercompensation* stage the body improves above baseline so it can better handle the next exercise stress it is given. In the case of weight training, the body increases in strength so that it can more easily handle the load being placed upon it.

You will notice that there is one more section of the periodization curve, *detraining* (or *involution*). In addition, we have added a *fatigue* curve represented by the dashed line. The fatigue curve can logically be correlated to Selye's *exhaustion* stage. As the stress is continually applied to the organism it becomes exhausted, has reduced capacity to respond, and falls below normal functioning levels. This very same response occurs if we continually apply an exercise stress without allowing sufficient recovery for adaptation. Unfortunately, this is quite common in our industrialized society where "more" is always considered "better". It is the major mistake made when we follow the "no pain, no gain" concept. We have been led to believe that soreness is an indication of a good workout, and that all exercises must be performed to failure to maximize gains. Both of these concepts are incorrect and often lead to either acute or overuse injuries.

> *Acute Injury:* an injury occurring as an immediate result of the overload.
> *Overuse Injury:* an injury resulting from the continued application of overload to a tissue already damaged from a previous training stimulus.

The association between Selye's curve and the *detraining* portion of the periodization curve is somewhat less apparent and may even be a bit of a stretch, but let's try. We noted that exercise, as a stress, is both a response and a stimulus. When exercise is removed for a sufficient time, the body has the capacity to restructure itself and therefore improve. This response is represented by the *compensation* and *supercompensation* portions of the periodization curve. If the stimulus (exercise) is removed for too long, the body will no longer feel the need to support the changes (in the case of weight training larger, stronger, and faster muscles) and will therefore allow the body to return to its unstressed, baseline level. To help you visualize the connection between Selye's GAS curve and the periodization curve we have placed both on the same graph (see Figure 9-3).

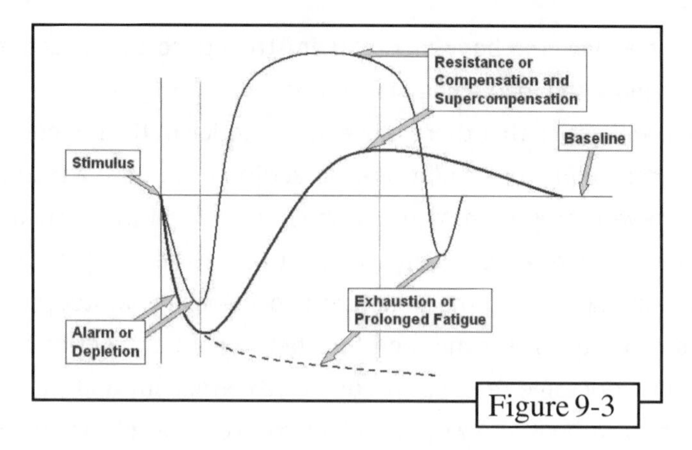

Figure 9-3

Some researchers and coaches have argued that using a single component, fatigue, to explain the shape of the periodization curve is too simplistic, since training not only generates fatigue (fatigue effect), it also stimulates an improvement in fitness (fitness effect). This *two-component model* argues that the shape of the curve is the result of adding together the fatigue and fitness effects. In Figure 9-4 we present both the fatigue and fatigue-fitness models so you can compare them.

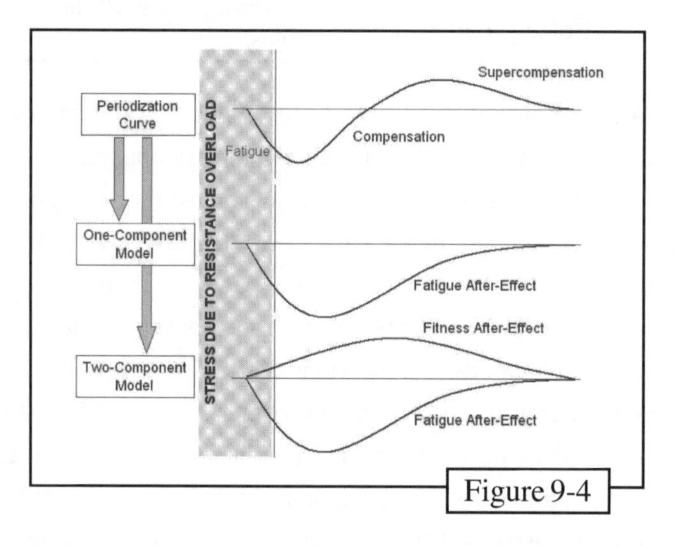

Figure 9-4

There are a number of factors that support this two-component model. First of all, it is not uncommon for individuals to show increases in performance during a second or third set of maximal lifting effort. This is especially true in trained athletes, where presumably the fatigue effect would be less drastic. Second, at the beginning of studies that employ controlled weight-training programs, individuals often show significant strength gains due to neurological improvements. Third, when training methods that target an energy system or muscle group are performed, the energy systems and muscle groups that are not targeted often show improvements even when the targeted muscle groups or systems are showing decrements. And finally, the patterns of fatigue and improvement vary differently according to the level of conditioning of the person training.

It should be recognized that this two-component model does not change the shape of the periodization curve, but rather offers an alternative explanation for its shape. In addition, it provides an explanation for the different responses we see in trained and untrained individuals when the same training stimulus is applied.

That's the background theory supporting the use of periodization. Multiple controlled studies, as well as practical application, have proven its superiority to standard progressive resistance training methods. Now let's look at applying periodization theory to training.

How to Manipulate the Curve (or How It Manipulates You!)

In Figure 9-5 we have redrawn the periodization curve but added two additional lines. These lines represent two of the major variables manipulated during training, *volume* and *intensity*. As you will recall from previous chapters, in weight training, *volume* is very simply the amount of total weight you have lifted in a training session or cycle. It can be computed using the formula:

Volume = Load lifted x Number of reps x Number of sets

The second line is the *intensity* of the workout. For weight training this has classically been expressed as the load used during an exercise. With current training concepts, such as power, speed and agility training, becoming more and more prominent among athletes and the general public, we should also add movement velocity to the definition. So intensity can also be considered the power output, where power is computed as:

Power = Load x Velocity

Regardless of the factor used to express intensity, the interactions among the volume, intensity, and the shape of the periodization curves remain the same.

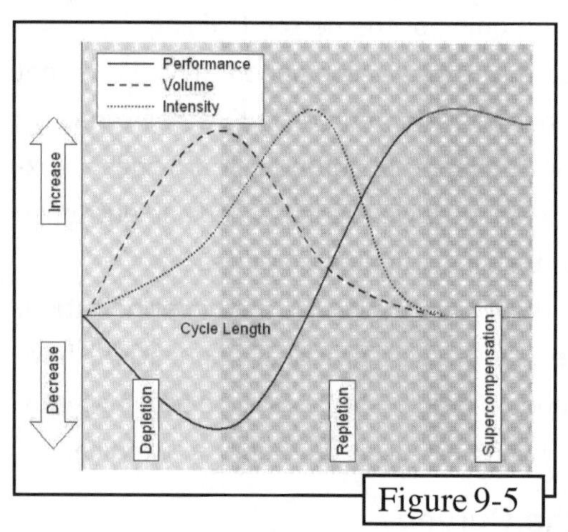

Figure 9-5

If you examine the curves you will notice that at the beginning of a cycle the intensity and the volume of work both rise. These increases cause *depletion* (performance falls). To allow *compensation* to occur, the *volume* of the work is then reduced (note the drop in the volume curve as the compensation stage begins). While this is occurring, the *intensity* of the work continues to rise. There is an important concept here that might slip by if we don't mention it. Intensity is the major stimulus for improvement, especially in strength and power activities like weight training. By reducing the *volume* of work while we continue to raise the *intensity*, we can stimulate improvement (fitness effect) while reducing the fatigue effect. This is seen in the *compensation* leg of the periodization curve. The final part of the process is to reduce the *intensity* of the work so that complete recovery and *supercompensation* can occur. Once this is done, a new training cycle can begin. Many of you who are athletes or who are familiar with the training patterns used in athletics may know this pattern as gradual volume reduction followed by a gradual reduction in intensity as *taper.*

A Basic Problem

Any time periodization theory is explained theoretically, some basic questions come up: "How long should a training cycle last?", "How should training techniques vary within a cycle?", "When should I begin to taper (reduce my training load)?" The answers to these and other questions are complicated by inconsistencies in the "vocabulary of periodization". Terms are often used interchangeably, and therefore, a term that implies a negative consequence to one person may be looked at as a positive stimulator by another. In an attempt to reduce this confusion we will define some terms and then use these terms to address the question of cycle length.

In their reviews of the topic of periodization a number of authors have attempted to clarify terms so that these terms will have a consistent meaning when used by trainers, researchers, athletes, and those of us who train for health and recreation.

We will use the following definitions in this text. You will recall that two of the most basic terms in exercise training theory are overload and adaptation. *Overload* is an outside stimulus, greater than the body's normal activity level, which tells the body to change. *Adaptation* is making the change in response to the specific overload. These terms enjoy almost universal acceptance among fitness professionals. The confusion comes when terms are simultaneously used to explain the process of periodization of training and the syndrome commonly termed overtraining. Many coaches, athletes and trainers use the term *overtraining* to describe a condition where the body requires an inordinate amount of time to recover from the applied overload. Others use terms like *staleness*, *overfatigue*, and *overstress* to describe this condition and argue that the term overtraining should actually be defined as training above the individual's normal capacity and is a necessary stimulus for improvement. Other practitioners and researchers have termed this level of overtraining, which requires only a short recovery period, *overreaching*. Other terms like *overstress*, *overstrain*, and *overtraining syndrome* have also found their way into the literature and vernacular of the training room.

For the purposes of this book we will adopt the following definitions when describing the periodization of training. *Overload* will be used to describe the stress applied during any training program and *fatigue* will be used to describe the reduced performance that results from that stress. *Overreaching* will be used to describe the process of applying an overload that results in a short-term (hours or days) reduction in performance. *Overtraining syndrome* will be used to describe a condition where the body cannot recover from the overload within a short period of time. Overtraining syndrome during weight training can commonly be diagnosed by the symptoms listed in Figure 9-6. Finally, we will use the term *injury* to refer to any tissue damage resulting from training overload. This term will then be further clarified by using modifiers that clarify the length (acute = immediate; chronic = long-term), location (tissue = gross structure such as the muscle, joint or connective tissue; ultrastructural = cellular level) or the cause (acute trauma = result of a single event; overuse = repeated stresses over a longer time period).

Symptoms of Overtraining

Sympathetic Form	Parasympathetic Form
• Decreased Performance	• Decreased Performance
• Prolonged Recovery	• Unaffected Recovery
• Quick or Chronic Fatigue	• Quick or Chronic Fatigue
• Increase in Perceived Exertion for Set Workload	• Mood Swings including Depression and Irritability
• Increased Resting Heart Rate	• Decreased Resting Heart Rate
• Sleep Disruption	• Sleep Disruption
• Sudden Weight Loss	• No Apparent Weight Loss

Figure 9-6

The Classic Time-Based Cycles

Training cycles are defined both by their length and the performance goals that they target. The classic terms used to define cycles using their length as the definitive factor are *microcycle, mesocycle,* and *macrocycle*. A *microcycle* (micro = small) can be defined as the pattern of work and recovery seen during a single week of training.

The term "linear" and "daily undulating" periodization have currently surfaced in the literature. Linear periodization has been defined as a progressive increase in intensity and reduction in volume throughout a training cycle, while daily undulating periodization is characterized by changes in intensity and volume during the microcycle. We believe that these terms are unnecessary, since a microcycle, as part of the periodization scheme, should by nature incorporate periods of "undulating" intensity and volume. In fact, you'll often hear experienced weight-trainers use terms like "heavy days" and "light days" to describe the cyclic change in training intensity and volume they are using during a specific week of training (see Figure 9-7).

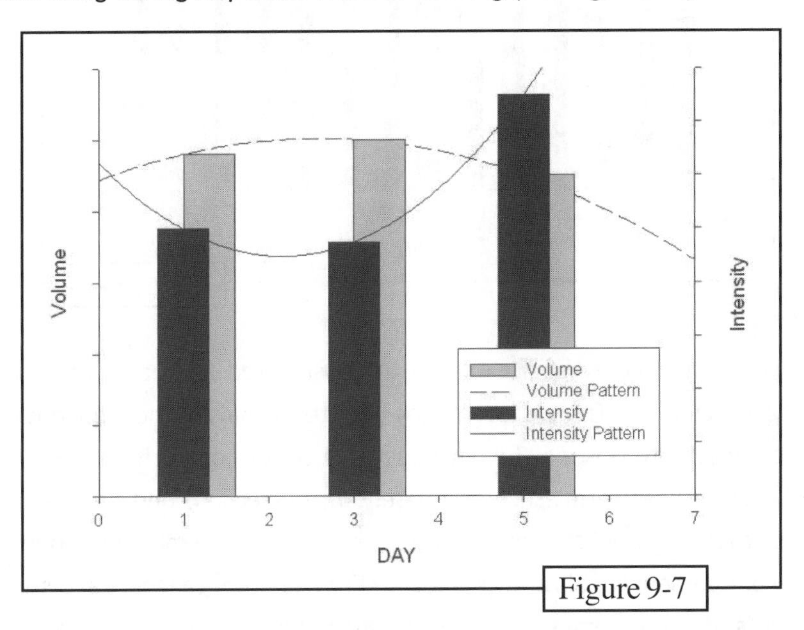

Figure 9-7

A *mesocycle* usually refers to a number of weeks of training strung together to create a cycle of longer duration. The term mesocycle is derived from the Greek *meso* or middle. The length of the mesocycle is between the length of a microcycle and a macrocycle. Therefore, the mesocycle is made up of a number of microcycles, and a number of mesocycles make up a macrocycle. The nature of a mesocycle is dictated by the nature of the microcycles that are used to construct it (see Figure 9-8). Another way of looking at this is to say that the nature of any individual microcycle will be dictated by where it is placed in the mesocycle and the desired pattern of change during that mesocycle.

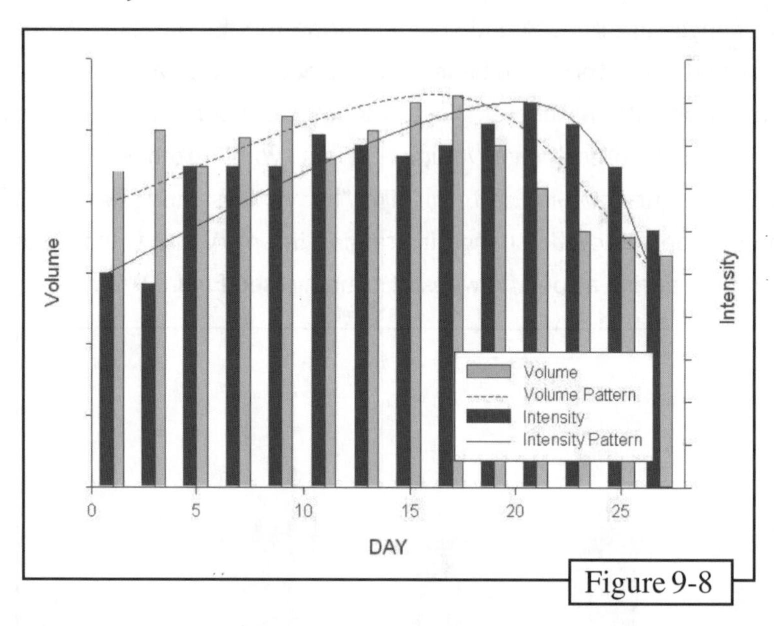

Figure 9-8

A *macrocycle* (macro = large) is constructed from a number of mesocycles. In effect it targets the long-term goals of the individual. For an athlete this may be defined by his or her competitive season. We often hear terms such as *off-season*, *preseason*, and *in-season*. For those of us who train for fitness the macrocycle may be defined by our personal goals and calendars. For example, teachers and students may use semesters to define individual macrocycles. Recreational athletes like skiers or softball players may use their specific playing seasons to define the nature and duration of their macrocycles. Regardless of the person who is training, the nature of any of these cycles will be controlled by individual goals and needs, level of fitness, and the social or professional constraints within which he or she must train. In Chapter 10 we will give specific examples of cycle lengths for different individuals with diverse needs and goals. It may be advisable to add one last comment here. Strength and conditioning professionals are continually experimenting with unique patterns of periodization. Many of these newer techniques blur the distinctions between cycles. This is not a problem as far as training but may complicate decisions and require further clarification when these patterns are being used and compared.

The Classic Purpose-Based Cycles

In addition to defining resistance training-based periodization cycles using their time durations, they can also be defined by their purpose. To avoid confusion, these purpose-based cycles are often termed *phases* or *blocks*. A number of different *phases* are commonly included in any resistance-training program. A phase may contain a number of microcycles and therefore be temporally defined as a mesocycle, or it may be defined as a macrocycle with a number of structured mesocycles designed to target a specific goal. For the purposes of this text we will be using individual mesocycles of 3-8 weeks as the building blocks for phases designed to target specific purposes. In addition, we will call these phases, cycles, since their time duration can clearly be stated, and we consider "purpose" a more meaningful and descriptive way of naming a cycle.

There are a number of common purpose-based cycles presented in the literature on periodization. The purposes, lengths, and training strategies employed during these cycles are diverse. A chart presenting samples of the purpose-based cycles described below is presented in Figure 9-9.

The Tissue Adaptation Cycle. The first cycle presented in any periodization program is usually a *hypertrophy* cycle; however, we would like to make a distinction in this text between a hypertrophy cycle and what we like to call a *tissue adaptation* cycle. A hypertrophy cycle is designed specifically to increase the size of a skeletal muscle, although tendons and bones are also affected. As we noted in Chapter 2, each of these tissues will hypertrophy at different rates of speed with the muscle showing increases within a few weeks, con-

Figure 9-9

SAMPLE CYCLES FOR OLDER INDIVIDUALS*

CYCLE	TISSUE ADAPTATION	STRENGTH	POWER	ENDURANCE
Sets	Sets	2-3	2-3	1-2
Repetitions	Repititions	8-10	8-12	25-30
Inensity (Load)	30-80% 1RM (Gradual increase)	75-80% 1RM	50-60% 1RM	35-40% 1RM
Duration	6-8 weeks	6-8 weeks	3-4 weeks	4-5 weeks
Transition cycle	none	3-4 weeks	2 weeks	2-3 weeks
Nature of the cycle	Lifts using slow concentric and eccentric movements	Lifts using slow concentric and eccentric movements	Low-inertia and band lifts, high speed concentric, low speed eccentric	Moderate-speed circuit training

* Note: these values can vary considerably based on the goals, age, training status, etc. of the individual.

nective tissue hypertrophying in about 6-8 weeks, and bone requiring between 6 months and a year. Along with the increase in size, there is usually an increase in the structural strength of the tissues, and this fact is the basis of the distinction between a hypertrophy and a tissue adaptation cycle. When we speak about structural strength, we are talking about the structural integrity of your tissues. Before you can ask your muscles and connective tissues to lift a load that will increase their strength and size substantially, you must gradually increase their structural integrity. It's like building a bridge. We've all seen those wooden suspension bridges built with vines and slats of wood in adventure movies. While these might hold the weight of a person, they certainly would not support a car, a truck, or the typical volume of traffic of our more impressive suspension bridges, like the George Washington or Golden Gate bridges. They would simply be damaged, if not destroyed, by the weight of the vehicles. To prevent this, engineers have designed the bridges with bigger and stronger cables that can support the weight of the traffic. This is the purpose of a tissue adaptation cycle. It gradually "re-engineers" your tissues so they can handle the stresses of training. This cycle is especially important for persons just beginning a program, those at risk for injury due to weakness (such as younger children with developing tissues, older persons with aging tissues, or people rehabilitating damaged tissues), those changing program intensity, or those returning to training after a period of detraining.

Very simply, the reason for a tissue adaptation cycle is to reduce the level of DOMS associated with a weight-training program (see chapter 2). To prevent a costly visit to your local sports medicine physician (who will inevitably tell you to stop training), you should gradually increase your load to allow your tissues to handle the stress. In other words, you should always include a cycle designed to increase tissue size and integrity when training intensity and/or volume are being significantly altered during a program. The key is to increase your program slowly, allowing adaptation and reducing injury. Therefore, since the primary purpose of this cycle is to increase the structural integrity of the tissues by increasing their cross-sectional area, we have chosen to call it a Tissue Adaptation Cycle. In this way we hope to distinguish it from a hypertrophy cycle, which has as its primary goal an increase in muscle size.

The Hypertrophy Cycle. As noted in the previous section, we are using the term *hypertrophy cycle* to define a cycle whose purpose is to increase the size of a skeletal muscle. While other connective tissues, such as bone, tendons and ligaments may also increase in cross-sectional area due to this training, the tissue targeted and assessed is most often the muscle itself. This phase may be used as a second preparatory phase prior to pure strength training, or it may have as its goal strictly to increase in size, as is the case with bodybuilders. In fact, the typical 8-12 repetition, multiple-set program so prevalent in the gym is a carry-over from the classic hypertrophy training used by bodybuilders.

To say that hypertrophy training is only appropriate for increasing muscle size and "sculpting" the body for competition, however, is to ignore a clinical use for this training cycle. Tissue loss is often the result of specific injuries or illnesses and also occurs as a natural consequence of aging. Among the most common examples of illness that produce atrophy are neuromuscular or immune system disorders. Even more common is the disuse atrophy that often accompanies immobilization or bed rest after a fracture or severe ligament damage. Age-related losses of muscle and bone are even more common and have the potential to affect every living person as he or she ages. Hypertrophy cycles have been used for years as part of a clinical intervention to combat atrophy and prepare the body for functional training to improve performance.

The Strength Cycle. The strength cycle may bear the most universally accepted name of all the purpose-based training cycles. It is the cycle designed to develop muscular strength. As you have seen in Chapter 4, there are a number of training strategies that can be utilized to develop strength depending on the specific goals and needs of the individual. These methods can be used to vary the training stimulus during the cycle. This serves two purposes. The first is to allow changes in the intensity and volume of the cycle, while varying the training pattern. Variations in the pattern of training have been shown to increase strength gains by changing the neuromuscular stimulus and incorporating the use of different synergists. The second advantage is that it can add variety to the training cycle and thereby reduce boredom.

This cycle often incorporates higher intensity (more resistance) and less volume (lower repetitions) than the hypertrophy cycle since its purpose is to force the body to adapt to greater loads. Therefore the stimulus would be more "load-based" than "volume-based", targeting strength rather than mass.

The Power or Speed-Strength Cycle. Of all the cycles that can be incorporated into a periodized weight-training program, perhaps the most controversial is the power or speed-strength cycle. While many coaches, trainers, therapists, and exercise scientists argue that the theory of speed-specificity dictates that power development requires high-speed resistance training as a primary stimulus, others strongly disagree. There is little doubt that both neurological and performance-based data support the use of high-speed, explosive movements to develop power. In addition, the long lever systems of the body (arms, legs, hips and shoulder) provide biomechanical support for explosive training and many authors have reported the importance of speed, rather than strength, as the most important factor in power production. However, some experts contend that performing high-speed exercises with external loads puts the individual at great risk for injury due to the inertia of the weights. These professionals argue that the place for power and speed development is outside the weight room and on the field, gymnasium floor, or track. As we stated earlier in this text, it is not our purpose in this book to attempt to solve nor take sides in this debate. However, we do believe that loading can be safely accomplished during high-speed movements, provided the problem of inertia is addressed, and the individual's tissues have been properly prepared for the overload. A quick review of Chapters 4 and 5 will reveal the training techniques and low-inertia loading devices which reduce the potential for injury during high-speed resistance training.

The Muscular Endurance Cycle. A final cycle, which may be included in the periodization model, is the *muscular endurance cycle*. We have chosen to use the term muscular endurance, rather than simple endurance, since we wish to distinguish the goal of this cycle from that of endurance training, which texts have often made synonymous with cardiovascular training. Muscular endurance can be defined as an individual's ability to maintain a particular power output (conversely fatigue is the inability to maintain that power output). We know that this is dependent on the intensity of the exercise since the muscle has to depend on a higher proportion of anaerobic energy production as intensity increases and the anaerobic systems are depleted more quickly than the aerobic systems. The purpose of the muscular endurance cycle is to decrease the levels of fatigue in the face of increasing loads. This is usually accomplished by using lower loads and increasing the number of repetitions.

Taper and Recovery

In the typical periodization literature, terms like recovery and active recovery are used to describe the reductions in load and intensity which mark the end of a specific training cycle. We have chosen to avoid these terms for several reasons. First of all, psychologically, recovery is often thought of as a cessation in training. We have seen that this concept has a negative effect on the willingness of individuals to apply periodization theory. While most athletes understand and utilize tapers (reductions in volume and ultimately intensity) to increase performance, recreational exercisers are seldom faced with the prospect of failing to perform maximally due to overtraining syndrome (because few of us ever perform maximally in any measured event). Therefore, recovery periods are often seen by the non-athlete as periods when they will lose the gains they have worked so hard to accomplish, even though this is not the case. In fact, some researchers have shown that lay-offs of 6-8 weeks caused strength loss of about 10%.

The second reason we tend to avoid the term recovery is because it is not descriptive of the taper period. We consider this period as a time of transition, when increased muscular capacity can be "translated" into performance that is meaningful to the individual. Therefore, we have chosen the term "translational cycle" to describe this active recovery period. This is not a unique idea, but merely an attempt to use a generic term to describe a strategy that has been used for years in athletics and should be employed by all of us to maximize the benefits of our training. Let us give you a very practical example. While American football players may spend hours in the weight room per week, the greatest percentage of their time is spent on the playing field "translating" the strength, speed, and power they have developed into functional performance appropriate for their game. In fact, as the competitive year progresses, a greater percentage of the time is spent honing their game skills and less time is spent in the weight room. So as intensity and volume drop during the end of a training cycle (tapering period), the concentration on skill-based (translational) training increases. This pattern is true of the macrocycle and the mesocycles and microcycle from which it is created. A third important aspect of the translational period is that it can be used as a period of reevaluation of the training regimen. Since training causes a change, the individual who is training is constantly evolving and his or her needs are evolving also. The translational period can be used to assess the new needs of the individual and plan the next training cycle to meet those needs.

This being the case, training and translational periods should not be considered to have clearly defined starting and stopping points, rather as you are tapering during one of your resistance-training cycles you can be can be increasing your concentration on practicing motor skills that are important to your goals (whether they be health, competition or recreational) (see Figure 9-10).

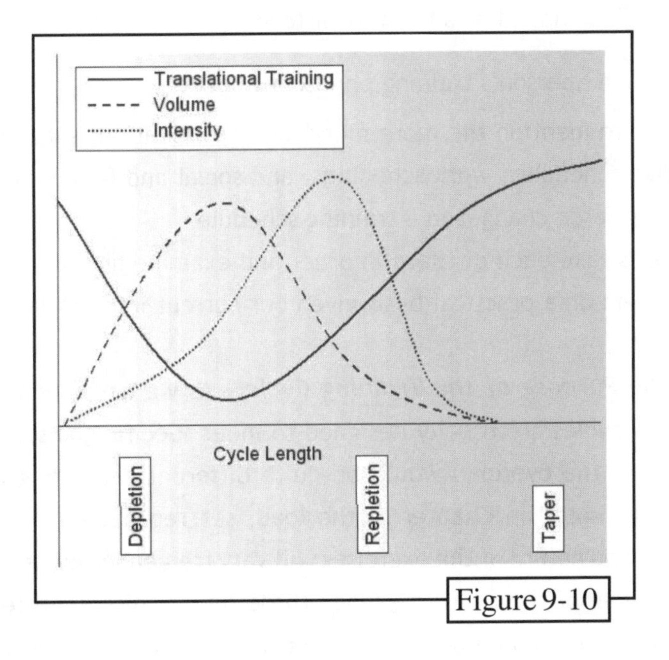

Figure 9-10

Practically Understanding Periodization

We have chosen this "play on words" as the subheading for the final section of this chapter because it indicates, in our opinion, the state of the art in the application of periodization training today. Now let's get back to those basic questions: "How long should a training cycle last?", "How should training techniques vary within a cycle?", "When should I begin to taper (reduce my training load)?"

These questions are not easily answered, since they are dependent on a number of factors including:

- The purpose of the training cycle;
- The current training status of the individual;
- The age or developmental status of the individual;
- Specific health considerations;
- The individual's training history;
- The person's training philosophy

Not to mention the more mundane considerations such as competitive schedules, work schedules, and social and family pressures that can force changes in a training schedule.

Let's take each of these in order and examine how we can deal with them on a practical basis given our current information on the topic.

The Purpose of the Training Cycle. As we have seen above, training cycles are usually designed to meet specific goals, and the nature of the overload would be quite different depending on the goal. As noted in Chapter 8, the load, set/rep pattern, recovery period, and nature of the exercises will vary tremendously depending on the goal of the training. Since these factors directly affect the intensity and volume of training, and intensity and volume dictate the shape of the training curve, we would expect the lengths of cycles targeting different goals to differ substantially.

This, in fact, is the case. More and more we are finding the old 4-week mesocycle is being scrapped for cycles that are designed based on measured or perceived levels of fatigue. Our research has shown that with older individuals, the tissue adaptation cycle required approximately 6-8 weeks, the hypertrophy cycle approximately 8 weeks, the strength cycle about 4-6 weeks, and the power cycle approximately 3-4 weeks. These cycle lengths, however, are based on preliminary data using the first sign of a performance deficit as an indicator of the need to begin the recovery potion of the cycle. We believe that much more work is required by scientists and practitioners before optimal cycle lengths can be provided for different training goals and different populations. Until these studies are completed, the cycle lengths used for our sample periodization programs, presented in Chapter 10, will be based on our analyses of the best scientific and empirical evidence we have to date.

The Current Training Status of the Individual. There is no doubt that the length of individual, targeted training cycles and the patterns of change in volume and intensity within these cycles are dependent on the current training status of the individual. This is true for a number of reasons. First of all, current research clearly shows that persons at low levels of training such as beginners, those returning from an off-season layoff, or persons returning to training after deconditioning resulting from an injury, are at much greater risk for injury if pre-layoff loads are used during the start of the new training period. Second, these individuals also show much greater levels of microscopic damage (DOMS) when returning to training, than individuals in a stable training status. Third, the lengths of the recovery periods required by persons at lower fitness levels would be greater. And fourth, the capacity of untrained or detrained individuals to handle both the intensity and volume of work would be lower than that of a trained individual. All of these factors would, of course, affect the nature of any periodization cycle regardless of its specific goal.

The Age or Developmental Status of the Individual. Although the capacity for building muscle may be greater in young individuals, especially after puberty, it is well maintained into old age. However, there are special considerations when prescribing exercise for these individuals. Since a younger person's muscles, bones, and connective tissues are still developing, they clearly have not yet reached their structural capacity. If we look to the other end of the spectrum, older people show reduced structural strength due to loss of muscle fibers and degeneration of connective tissues, including bone. Each of these groups requires programs designed with these considerations in mind. We will examine these considerations in our program designs for each of these groups presented in Chapter 10.

Specific Health Considerations. We use the term specific health considerations in place of the more common term special populations. We prefer this term rather than special populations since the theme of this text is based on the premise that each individual has his or her own unique goals and needs and so constitutes a special case within the population (Weight Training Everyone!). The term special health considerations recognizes the fact that some individuals may have structural or metabolic issues that further dictate a specific pattern of change in their periodization program. Conditions such as osteoporosis, injury or disease-related atrophy, chronic back pain, and preexisting musculoskeletal weakness are structural considerations that modify any periodization plan. Additionally, metabolic concerns such as diabetes and obesity might modify both the goal and nature of the program. While it is not the intention of this book to be a training guide for special populations, Chapter 10 will provide some examples of periodization programs designed to address metabolic concerns.

The Individual's Training History. While training history may seem very much like training status, there is a subtle difference. A person may have an extensive training history, but currently he or she may not be training, and therefore, may have a training status far below what might be expected from his or her training history. Such situations present a special challenge both physiologically and psychologically. Physiologically we know that tissues have a "memory" and can therefore maintain functional performance for a long time after formal training has ceased, especially in active individuals. However, this "stored capacity" is often overestimated by the lifter, his or her training partner, and even a personal trainer. While it is true that an individual with an impressive training history may maintain a large amount of strength, remember that the structural integrity of the muscles, bones, and connective tissue must be reestablished before serious training can begin again. If we fail to include a tissue adaptation cycle and hypertrophy cycle prior to a strength cycle, we substantially increase the possibility of structural damage and injury.

The Person's Training Philosophy. To best explain this concept perhaps a story would be best. A subject in one of our studies, who we will call Joe (or we could call him David, which is also a very nice name) loved training on our resistance-training equipment so much and was so amazed by his own progress, that when it came time for him to taper during the recovery phase of his hypertrophy cycle, he refused. His philosophy was that the level of training he was performing had gotten him to the fitness level where he was, and that reducing his training in any way, or changing it, would ruin all his hard work. It took nearly two weeks of explanation and presentation of results from multiple studies to get Joe to begin a translational period designed to allow his muscles to recover and for us to introduce motor patterns that would translate his new strength into functional movement patterns designed to meet his goals and needs. Once this was done, Joe began to see even greater improvements that created an even greater positive impact on his life. Needless to say when we wanted to begin the new resistance training cycle, Joe once again refused, contending that it was this translational training that had really impacted his life and that he wanted only this type of training program. Joe finally agreed after a thorough explanation of our training philosophy to give periodization cycling a chance, which resulted in a three-year program that both he and the graduate students in charge of the training, thoroughly enjoyed.

This story is not a criticism of Joe. In fact, more of us should think like him. When we design a program, or have one designed for us, we should always be asking why. Why am I performing this exercise? Why should I use this lifting pattern? Why should I be in a strength cycle rather than an endurance, hypertrophy or power cycle? Why start this recovery period now rather than a week or two sooner or one week later? Each of these questions is justified and reflects an attempt to develop a training philosophy than can evolve with your needs, goals and training status.

Cycle Lengths Are Not Carved in Stone

The sections above describe a number of factors that may affect the nature of an individual training cycle. The take-home message from these sections is that you should recognize that training cycles are being applied to living human beings with different genetic potentials, outside stresses, perceived exertion levels, and training states. In addition, not all cycles with the same title are equal. For example, the nature of a power cycle for a football or rugby player (strength dominant power) would be very different than that for a tennis player or golfer (speed dominant power). Therefore the intensity levels, training volumes, and cycle length should vary considerably.

How do we know if a cycle is lasting too long, is too intense, or is volume too high? The best bet is to examine markers that "tip us off" that change is necessary. While a number of markers (see figure 9-6) have been used to diagnose overtraining syndrome, only a few are both appropriate for resistance training assessment, cost effective, and non-invasive. The primary markers that fall into this classification are:

- Increased perceived exertion at a set workload;
- Inability to complete a set of exercise at a weight previously handled with minor difficulty.
- Quick or chronic fatigue;
- Mood swings;
- And to a lesser extent, reduced immune function and sleep disruptions.

This is not to say that every time you can't sleep or you become angry or depressed you're overtrained. What we are saying, however, is that if you are feeling perceived weakness, prolonged fatigue or a number of these symptoms, consider that they may be indicators that a taper is necessary, and don't allow our suggestions or someone else's "calendar of expectations" to force you into a state of overtraining where you may require a prolonged recovery, or even worse, suffer an acute or overuse injury.

Conclusion

Just a final thought as we end this chapter. Although periodization of training may feel uncomfortable at first, it has been proven as the best technique for maximizing improvement, reducing overtraining and injury, and maintaining long-term goals. We must reset our thought patterns and no longer consider a reduction in training an indication of failure or laziness, but a physiological and psychological necessity if we are to get the most we can out of our training.

Chapter

10

Sample Workouts

Now that we have presented the theories that govern resistance training programs, available exercises, specific training protocols, and periodization theory, let's look at some sample workouts which apply these concepts. The workouts included in this chapter are by no means all the possible workouts that can be performed. Also, by now, you should recognize that any workout provided can be modified to be better tailored for your specific needs.

The workouts included in this chapter can be divided into two categories. The first are workouts for specific types of athletes. We have included three classifications here. The first are athletes who participate in contact sports. The second are non-contact sport performers. The third are recreational athletes. Once again, these are general classifications that concentrate on strength-based sports; therefore we have also included a workout for endurance athletes.

The second set of workouts provided are for the general population and include a workout for weight loss, a workout for older individuals, and a general strength and conditioning workout.

We will preface each workout with an explanation concerning the reason for its structure. Additionally, you will note that all workouts use four mesocycles: hypertrophy to increase muscle and connective tissue size and strength, stregth to improve force production, power to increase the rate of force production, and endurance to improve your ability to maintain a specific power output.

Athlete Training

Over the past several decades, strength and conditioning have become a mainstay of most athletic programs around the world. There are two major differences between athletic conditioning and general health and fitness programs. First, you will notice that athletes tend to do considerably more work, or volume than lifters targeting health and fitness benefits. Typically an athlete will perform exercises that use heavier weights, more frequently, with more sets, and often with less recovery time. Secondly, the athlete will generally employ some form of explosive training using barbells, dumbbells, and other heavier resistance training pieces. However, since power and speed are important functional factors in many population, these individuals are now including some form of explosive training in their regular workouts.

Since training to be like an athlete is demanding and requires a base level of strength and many movements require considerable skill to perform safely, we felt it would be appropriate to separate the explosive lifts used by athletes from the regular strength training movements found in Chapter 6. Therefore, these lifts are presented below as part of the athletic performance workout section.

Explosive Lifts

While they tend to have "a bad rep" because of their complexity, explosive lifts, especially the Olympic lifts, are considered fundamental and required exercises for athletes by many strength and conditioning coaches. However, two very important elements should be considered when trying to incorporate these lifts into your program: time and practice. It takes many hours of repetitive work to perfect these movements, develop correct techniques, and establish the strength base necessary to avoid injury. In fact, we do not recommend adding any of the explosive lifts to your training program without first consulting a trainer or coach who has experience in teaching them. While we advocate using power movements in training, we cannot stress the importance of proper progression, using light weights to learn proper form before increasing your training load. Additionally, for those of you who do not have the time to develop proficiency in these lifts, remember that there are alternatives such as hydraulic or pneumatic machines, elastic bands and tubes, and high-speed aquatic movements.

In both Olympic lifts and their "partial" counterparts, the key element is speed while incorporating a precise technical movement. The reason for performing these lifts is to teach the body to develop the rapid muscle fiber recruitment patterns needed to generate hip speed and power. Contrary to common belief, these exercises are not meant for upper back and arm development. When performing any explosive lifts with a barbell or dumbbell, the bar should remain close to the body (which in turn keeps it close to the center line of force production) throughout the entire range of movement. Explosive lifts are also characterized by the fact that once the barbell is set in motion, it must be "caught". Catching, or "racking" as it is sometimes called, is the act of pulling the body under the barbell against the force of the bar moving upward. One of the most important factors to be considered during these lifts is to begin with a controlled stage (do not jerk) and then shift to a high-speed "hard pull" stage.

There are two fundamental kinds of pulls that coaches often use. When the word "Power" precedes the exercise such as Power Clean, the barbell starts on the floor. If the word "Hang" is used as in Hang Snatch, the barbell "hangs" in the starting position just above the knees. Additionally, there are two hand-grip placements: close or "clean" grip; and far, or "snatch" grip. Finally, to confuse things more, there are two basic foot-stances to "catch" the bar: standard (has no fancy name) where the feet end slightly wider than shoulder width, and the "Jerk" stance, where the feet land staggered almost in a lunge position.

So there you have it. From there, you can create lifts, such as the clean and jerk, power clean, and various forms of overhead presses such as the snatch press.

Push Press

Although this lift is similar to a military press, this exercise incorporates greater hip and upper body power transfer. The movement starts by generating power at the hips and driving the weight up through the upper body. The movement is initiated by a powerful pre-stretch dipping action like that used in jumping.

Figure 10-1

Position

Start by removing a bar from a shoulder height rack and placing it across the clavicle with a shoulder width grip. Step back from the rack maintaining a tight torso keeping the head and chest up.

Performance

Rapidly dip down, as if to jump, and then drive upward as fast as possible by completely extending the hips and knees. While in hip and knee extension, rapidly press the weight to full arm extension ending with the barbell overhead.

Figure 10-2a

Power Clean

The power clean is perhaps one of the best known and frequently used of all the power-based lifts.

Figure 10-2b

Grip Placement

The proper grip for performing the Power Clean is to grasp the bar slightly wider than shoulder width. For most athletes, one inch inside of the smooth part of the bar is adequate. Depending on the athlete's flexibility the grip position might need to be modified slightly, for comfort reasons.

Ready Position

Begin by placing the bar on the floor and positioning it so it touches the shins. Grasp the bar with the grip described above. The feet should be shoulder width apart. The head should be up, the chest out and the shoulders back. The back should be flat with a slight arch at the base. At this point the ankles, hips and knee joints are flexed. The shoulders should be positioned over the bar, and the arms should be straight.

The Movement

This lift must be performed as explosively as possible. To do this, begin by rapidly extending the ankles, knees, and hips at the same rate. As your legs approach full extension, powerfully shrug your trapezius muscles. Also as your legs approach full extension, powerfully pull your elbows up, while keeping them in a position over the bar. As the body becomes fully extended, extend your ankles.

The Catch

After the bar reaches sternum level, and the body is fully extended, rapidly lower the body under the bar. Rotate the elbows forward, extend the wrists and slightly raise the shoulders to cushion the bar landing on the shoulders. After the bar is caught on the shoulders, accelerate the body out of the bottom position. Once the bar has started upwards thrust the hips forward to place them under the bar. Once the bar is moving, begin to exhale through the mouth. Keep the muscles of the torso contracted throughout the ascent phase of the lift. Come to full knee lockout.

Recovery

After a standing position is achieved, drop the bar back to the floor in a controlled manner.

Power Snatch

Figure 10-3a

This exercise is one that requires extreme discipline, tremendous explosion, and cat-like reflexes for proper performance. Again, as was the case with the clean, proper technique (where the bar remains tight to the body) and movement (hip drive) make this an effective tool in developing athletic power.

Grip Placement

Figure 10-3b

To measure optimal grip extend one arm, with the hand in a closed fist, laterally so that it is parallel to the floor while the other arm hangs down the side of the body. Measure the distance from the outside of the shoulder of the hanging arm to the knuckles of the extended arm. This is the correct distance between the index fingers when grasping the bar.

Ready Position

Like in the Power clean, begin by placing the bar on the floor and positioning it touching the shins. Grasp the bar using the grip described above. The feet should be shoulder width apart. The head should be up, the chest out and the shoulders back. The back should be flat with a slight arch at the base. At this point the ankles, hips and knee joints will be flexed. The shoulders should be positioned over the bar, and the arms should be straight.

The Movement

This part of the lift is also very similar to that of the Power Clean. This phase must be performed as explosively as possible. To do this, begin by rapidly extending the ankles, knees, and hips at the same rate. As your legs approach full extension, powerfully shrug your trapezius muscles. Also, as your legs approach full extension, powerfully pull your elbows up, while keeping them in a position over the bar. As the body becomes fully extended, extend your ankles.

The Catch

This is the most difficult part of the movement and will take much practice before the lifter feels entirely comfortable performing with it. After the bar reaches sternum level and the body is fully extended, rapidly lower the body under the bar. Next, rotate the elbows forward and push up against the bar. Fully extend the arms so that the wrist, arm, and shoulder form a straight line. After the arms are fully extended, accelerate the body out of the bottom position. Once the bar has started upwards thrust the hips forward to place them under the bar. When the bar is moving at a sufficient speed, exhale through the mouth. Keep the muscles of the torso contracted through out the ascent phase of the lift. Come to full knee lockout.

Recovery

After a standing position is achieved, drop the bar back to the floor in a controlled manner.

Other Pulls

A variety of upper body pulls are often used when training athletes. Some of the pulls are designed to improve strength, while others are used to help teach the explosive lifts and improve mechanics. The bent over barbell row (figure 10-4), upright row (10-5) and high pull (10-6) are all pulling motions that require significant contributions by the latissimus dorsi, trapezius, rhomboids, and biceps. The bent over row is an explosive lift concentrating on the trapezius and rhomboids. The upright row is used to improve strength that will aid in the clean and

Figure 10-4

snatch exercises, as well as develop the postural muscles, neck muscles and trap muscles that are all important in many sports. The high pull is the same movement as the upright row only it is done explosively with help from the legs and hips.

Figure 10-5

Position

Maintain proper back and chest position. Your chin should be up and your head should be in line with your back. Do not hyperextend your neck. Your arms should be fully extended and barbell gripped at either the clean or snatch position.

Performance

Pull your arms up and in toward your sternum. Keep the torso tight until the bar touches the sternum or slightly higher. Hold this position for a 1 count (except in the high pull) and then slowly lower the bar back to full arm extension.

Figure 10-6

Step-Ups

This is a great exercise to develop hip strength, knee strength, and balance. Like many of these more complex exercises, you should practice with little or no weight and develop proper technique before progressing to heavier weights and higher boxes. Start with a 6 inch box and then progress up to 18 inches. The box should never be much higher than a point where the thigh is parallel to the ground.

Figure 10-7

Position

Stand upright with the bar across your back (as in squat) or weights in hands. Keep your head up and chest out to maintain proper back alignment. Step up so your entire foot is on the box (your leg should be about parallel). Your front leg should be in a similar position as a squat with the knee never coming over the toe.

Performance

Press down on the box with your lead foot to develop the force necessary to extend the knee and hips. You should not push from the back leg. Pull your trail leg up until you are completely extended and either place the trail leg on the box (for balance) or begin the descent. You may drag it along the box for greater stability. Slowly descend the trail leg back down emphasizing the negative. Maintain proper back alignment during the lift. You may alternate legs or do all your reps with the same leg.

The Workouts

As you begin to look over the workouts you will notice a pattern or as explained in chapter 9, a periodized training scheme. We have included various training cycles or training programs for each of the groups discussed above. Following the general periodized approach, you will find a progression that takes the trainee through workouts that address each of the components of a complete resistance training program.

The Contact-Sport Athlete

A contact sport athlete needs size, power, and strength. Since time is usually an issue these athletes generally perform multi-joint, multi-plane movements. In today's competitive sporting world, more teams are concentrating on speed and power rather than size. A major consideration for these athletes is the emphasis on the trapezius and upper back work that also involves strengthening of the neck and of course the muscles used for running and jumping. Remember that the cycles presented here are used following an initial adaptation or general conditioning period, which is often relatively short in the elite athlete.

Hypertrophy Mesocycle-Contact Sport
Microcycle 1
Weeks 1-4

While this mesocycle concentrates on hypertrophy training, this training is usually combined with conditioning and skill work. Exercises emphasize major joint movements on the same day and work other aspects such as speed, or skill acquisition on the "off" days.

3x week, Monday, Wednesday, Friday, 3 sets 12 reps each exercise

Leg Press
Hamstring Curl
Lat Pulldown
Abdominal Crunches
Lunge
Benfh Press
Dips
Chin Ups

Microcycle 2
Weeks 5-8

3x week, Monday, Wednesday, Friday, 3 sets 12 reps each exercise

Deadlift
Hamstring Curl
Incline Dumbbell Press
Abdominal Crunches
Step Ups
Cable Row
Military Press
Upright Row

Microcycle 3
Weeks 9-12

3x week, Monday, Wednesday, Friday, 3 sets 10 reps each exercise

Squat
Leg Curl
Incline Bench Press
Close Grip Bench Press
Abdominal Crunches
Leg Extenstion
Chin Ups
Barbell Row

Recovery Week
Week 13

2x week, Tuesday Thursday, 3 sets 6 reps each exercise

Squat
Bench Press
Lat Pulldown

The goal of the recovery week is to work the major muscles but use very little volume. Usually during this week an athlete will have a quick workout using weights, spend extra time stretching, conditioning, or just playing a recreational sport. In many cases, resistance training will be dropped altogether. Unlike the transition periods incorporated into our senior population workouts these recovery periods are recovery oriented. Since athletes generally train and practice 5 or 6 times a week and include their movement skills, balance, and plyometrics as part of their training cycle, we use this time to reduce total training volume and allow for additional recovery.

Strength Mesocycle-Contact Sport

Microcycle 1
Weeks 1-4

The Strength phase is characterized by heavy lifting splits where specific multi- joint pushing, pulling and leg work are separated. Also, during this time, athletes spend less time working on movement skills and conditioning.

2x week, Monday, Thursday (3 x 8), 2x week, Tuesday, Friday (3x 8)

Bench
Incline Dumbbell
Lat Pulldown
Cable Row
Barbell Military Press
Dumbbell Bicep Curl
Triceps Pushdown

Press Leg Press
Bench Press Lunge
Leg Extension
Leg Curl
Seated Calf raise
Abdominal Crunch

Microcycle 2
Weeks 5-8

2x week, Monday, Thursday (3 x 8) 2x week, Tuesday, Friday (3 x 8)

Incline Bench Press
Close Grip Bench Press
Chin Ups
Dumbbell Row
Upright Row
Barbell Curl
Skull Crusher

Squat
Lunge
Leg Extension
Back Hyperextensions
Heel Raise
Hip Raise

Microcycle 3
Weeks 9-12

2x week, Monday, Thursday (4x 6), 2x week, Tuesday, Friday (4x 6)

Dumbbell Bench Press
Dips
Pull Ups
Barbell Row
Dumbbell Military Press
Lateral Raise
Straight Bar Curl
Triceps Kickback

Squat
Dead Lift
Step Up
Leg Extension
Leg Curl
Single Heel Raise
Twisting Abdominal Crunch

Unloading Week
Week 13

2x week, Tuesday Thursday, 3 sets 6 reps each exercise

Dead Lift
Dumbbell Bench Press
Barbell Row

Power Mesocycle-Contact Sport

Microcycle 1
Weeks 1-4

The power cycle is considered by most coaches to be the most important aspect of the resistance training program. Usually, these periods are combined with plyometric and other explosive work on the same days as the resistance training.

2x week, Monday, Thursday (4x 6), 2x week, Tuesday, Friday (4 x 6)

Hang Clean
Squat
Lunge
Leg Extension
Glute Ham Raise
Seated Calf Raise

Push Jerk
Bench Press
Barbell Row
Dumbbell Military Press
Upright Row
Abdominal Crunch

Microcycle 2
Weeks 5-8

2x week, Monday, Thursday (4x 6) 2x week, Tuesday, Friday (4x 6)

High Pull (explosive upright row)
Dead Lift
Step Up
Seated Leg Curl
Heel raise
Twisting Crunch

Hang Snatch
Incline Bench Press
Chin Up
Military Press
Lateral Raise

Microcycle 3
Weeks 9-12

2x week, Monday, Thursday (5x 4) 2x week, Tuesday, Friday (5x 4)

1 Arm Snatch
Squat
Lunge
Leg extension
Glute Ham Raise
Hip Raise

Power Clean
Close Grip Bench Press
Lat Pull Down
Barbell Military Press
Upright Row

Unloading Week
Week 13

2x week, Tuesday Thursday, 3 sets 6 reps each exercise

Incline Bench Press
Cable Row
Lunge

Endurance Mesocycle-Contact Sport

Microcycle 1
Weeks 1-4

Most likely, in the strength and conditioning facilities around the country, you will see this phase called conditioning. Exercise sets employ short rest periods, high energy, and quick workouts that may be set up in circuits. Some other cardiovascular form of conditioning is generally added as often as 6 times per week. Some contact sports such as soccer will run the full 12 week cycle, while many other will condense this to 6 or even 4 weeks.

3x week, Monday, Wednesday, Friday, 4 sets 15 reps each exercise

Leg Press
Seated Hamstring Curl
Lat Pulldown
Lunge
Bench Press
Twisting Crunch

Microcycle 2
Weeks 5-8

3x week, Monday, Wednesday, Friday, 4 sets 15 reps each exercise

Dead Lift
Lying Hamstring Curl
Incline Bench Press
Step Up
Chin Ups
Hip Raise

Microcycle 3
Weeks 9-12

3x week, Monday, Wednesday, Friday, 4 sets 18 reps each exercise

Squat
Dumbbell Bench Press
Abdominal Crunches
Lunge
Barbell Row

Unloading Week
Week 13

2x week, Tuesday Thursday, 3 sets 6 reps each exercise

Incline Dumbbell Press
Chin Ups
Step Ups

Non-Contact Sport Athlete

In general, the training of all athletes is similar. It is necessary to develop strength, speed and power. But since these athletes do not worry about collisions, explosive lifts are shifted to general movements performed rapidly. Olympic lifts are usually not included in the training program, upper trap work is reduced, and machine-based training represents are larger portion of the program.

Hypertrophy Mesocycle-Non-Contact Sport
Microcycle 1
Weeks 1-4

Hypertrophy training for these athletes is treated just like contact sport athletes.

3x week, Monday, Wednesday, Friday, 3 sets 12 reps each exercise

Dumbbell Lunge
Seated Hamstring Curl
Machine Bench Press
Abdominal Crunches
Leg Press
Bicep Curl
Lat Pulldown
Triceps Pushdown

Microcycle 2
Weeks 5-8

3x week, Monday, Wednesday, Friday, 3 sets 12 reps each exercise

Abdominal Crunches
Mechine Shoulder Pres
Lying Hamstring Curl
Dumbbell Bench Press
Cable Row
Leg Extension
Step Ups

Microcycle 3
Weeks 9-12

3x week, Monday, Wednesday, Friday, 3 sets 10 reps each exercise

Leg Extension
Seated Leg Curl
Incline Dumbbell Bench Press
Abdominal Crunches
Squat
Machine Row
Lateral Raise

Unloading Week
Week 13

2x week, Tuesday Thursday, 3 sets 6 reps each exercise

Squat
Machine Bench Press
Lat Pulldown

Strength Mesocycle-Non-Contact Sport
Microcycle 1
Weeks 1-4

The focus is to improve overall strength with emphasis placed on specific muscles that are used in that sport. Strength-training exercises targeting sport-specific muscles are generally performed with machines or tubes.

2x week, Monday, Thursday (3 x 8)

Machine Bench Press
Incline Dumbbell Bench Press
Lat Pulldown
Cable Row
Machine Shoulder Press
Dumbbell Bicep Curl
Triceps Pushdown

2x week, Tuesday, Friday (3 x 8)

Leg Press
Dumbbell Lunge
Leg Extension
Seated Leg Curl
Seated Calf Raise
Abdominal Crunch

Microcycle 2
Weeks 5-8

2x week, Monday, Thursday (3 x 8)	*2x week, Tuesday, Friday (3 x 8)*
Incline Machine Bench Press	Squat
Dumbbell Fly	Lunge
Assisted Chin Ups	Leg Extension
Machine Back Extension	Machine Row
Lateral Raise	Heel Raise
Hammer Curl	Hip Raise
Skull Crusher	

Microcycle 3
Weeks 9-12

2x week, Monday, Thursday (4 x 6)	*2x week, Tuesday, Friday (4 x 6)*
Dumbbell Bench Press	Leg Press
Assisted Dips	Dead Lift
Assisted Pull Ups	Step Up
Barbell Row	Leg Extension
Dumbbell Military Press	Lying Leg Curl
Lateral Raise	Single Heel Raise
Straight Bar Curl	Twisting Abdominal
Triceps Kickback	Crunch

Unloading Week
Week 13

2x week, Tuesday Thursday, 3 sets 6 reps each exercise

Dead Lift
Dumbbell Bench Press
Machine Row

Power Mesocycle-Non-Contact Sport

Microcycle 1
Weeks 1-4

While we generally do not prescribe the Olympic lifts for these athletes, we still concentrate on increased movement speed. Choose weights carefully so momentum and jerking don't negatively affect form during the movements.

2x week, Monday, Thursday (4x 6) 2x week, Tuesday, Friday (4x6)

Squat
Lunge
Leg Extension
Back Extension
Seated Calf Raise
Abdominal Crunch

Bench Press
Barbell Row
Dumbbell Military Press
Triceps Extension
Biceps Curl

Microcycle 2
Weeks 5-8

2x week, Monday, Thursday (4x 6) 2 x week, Tuesday, Friday (4x 6)

Dead Lift
Step Up
Seated Leg Curl
Heel raise
Twisting Crunch

Incline Bench Press
Assisted Chin Up
Machine Shoulder Press
Lateral Raise

Microcycle 3
Weeks 9-12

2x week, Monday, Thursday (5 x 4) 2x week, Tuesday, Friday (5 x 4)

Incline Dumbbell Bench Press
Lunge
Leg extension
Machine Back Extension
Heel Raise
Hip Raise

Squat
Lat Pull Down
Dumbbell Military Press
Triceps Extension
Biceps Curl

Unloading Week
Week 13

2x week, Tuesday Thursday, 3 sets 6 reps each exercise

Incline Bench Press
Cable Row
Lunge

Endurance Mesocycle-Non-Contact Sport

Microcycle 1
Weeks 1-4

Again, like the contact sport athletes, endurance training mesocycle duration will vary greatly by sport. Sports like tennis may use a full twelve week program to improve overall conditioning levels while a sport like volleyball may only use a 4-6 week version of this program.

3x week, Monday, Wednesday, Friday, 4 sets 15 reps each exercise

Seated Hamstring Curl
Machine Bench Press
Twisting Crunch
Leg Press
Leg Extension
Lat Pulldown

Microcycle 2
Weeks 5-8

3x week, Monday, Wednesday, Friday, 4 sets 15 reps each exercise

Lying Hamstring Curl
Incline Dumbbell Bench Press
Assisted Chin Ups
Dead Lift
Step Up
Hip Raise

Microcycle 3
Weeks 9-12

3x week, Monday, Wednesday, Friday, 4 sets 18 reps each exercise

Squat
Bench Press
Abdominal Crunches
Lunge
Barbell Row

Unloading Week
Week 13

2x week, Tuesday Thursday, 3 sets 6 reps each exercise

Incline Dumbbell Press
Assisted Chin Ups
Step Ups

The Endurance Athlete

The old thinking was that strength training would increase muscle size and the additional bulk would interfere with running speed. Scientific studies and empirical data, however, have shown that weight-training can increase running economy, improve times and reduce injury if applied correctly. Many athletes and coaches have adopted the concept of resistance training, with fear in their hearts. Their programs reflect this fear since they use high-repetition/low resistance sets. Our program reflects a periodized program using a hypertrophy phase to prepare the muscle and connective tissues for the mechanical overload of both resistance training and running, a strength phase to increase running efficiency, a power phase for explosiveness and stored elastic energy, and finally an endurance phase to increase muscular endurance.

Hypertrophy Mesocycle-Endurance Athlete

Microcycle 1
Weeks 1-4

This phase is designed to improve overall technique and adapt the tissues to the eccentric stresses associated with distance running.

2x week, Monday, Thursday, 2 sets 12-15 reps each exercise

Squat
Superman
Bicep Curl
Shrugs or Upright Rows
Toe Raises
Hip Extension
Hamstring Curl
Machine Bench Press
Triceps Extension
Standing Heel Raises
Hip Flexion
Abdominal Crunches

Microcycle 2
Weeks 5-8

2x week, Monday, Thursday, 2 sets 12-15 reps each exercise

Dumbbell Lunge
Dumbbell Bench Press
Deadlift or Hamstring Curl
Lying Hamstring Curl
Cable Row
Bicep Curl

Triceps Extension
Standing Heel Raises
Step Ups
Abdominal Crunches

Shrugs or Upright Rows
Toe Raises
Hip Extension

Microcycle 3
Weeks 9-12

2x week, Monday, Thursday 2 sets 10 reps each exercise

Squat
Bent-over Row
Barbell Bench Press
Step Ups

Deadlift
Standing Heel Raise
Upright Row
Abdominal Crunches

Unloading Week
Week 13

1x week, Tuesday Thursday, 2 sets 8 reps each exercise

Squat
Standing Heel Raise
Step Ups

Strength Mesocycle-Endurance Athlete

Microcycle 1
Weeks 1-4

Now that the tissues have been adapted, this cycle will increase strength and associated muscle economy, endurance, and elastic storage capacity.

2x week, Monday, Thursday (3x 6-10) 2x week, Tuesday, Friday (3x 6-10)

Bench Press
Bent-over Row
Triceps Extension
Cable Row
Upright Row
Bicep Curl
Abdominal Crunch

Squat
Dead Lift
Heel Raise
Toe Raise
Step Up
Hip Extension

Microcycle 2
Weeks 5-8

2x week, Monday, Thursday (3 x 8) 2x week, Tuesday, Friday (3 x 8)

Bench Press
Bent-over Row
Skull Crusher
Cable Row
Upright Row
Bicep Curl
Abdominal Crunch

Squat
Dead Lift
Heel Raise
Toe Raise
Step Up
Hip Extension

Microcycle 3
Weeks 9-12
2x week, Monday, Thursday (3 x 6) 2x week, Tuesday, Friday (3 x 6)

Bench Press
Bent-over Row
Skull Crusher
Cable Row
Upright Row
Bicep Curl
Abdominal Crunch

Squat
Dead Lift
Heel Raise
Toe Raise
Step Up
Hip Extension

Unloading Week
Week 13

2x week, Tuesday Thursday, 3 sets 6 reps each exercise
Squat
Heel Raise
Step Up

Power Mesocycle- Endurance Athlete
Microcycle 1
Weeks 1-4

Power cycles should employ free weights or tubing since we will concentrate on the velocity rather then the strength end of the load-velocity curve. We suggest that the load used be approximately 15-20% percent lower than the repetition figure would dictate. Here we present a thirteen week cycle; however, you may feel free to reduce the duration of this cycle depending on your training schedule.

2x week, Monday, Thursday (4 x 6) 2x week, Tuesday, Friday (4 x6)

Squat
Leg Curl
Step up
Standing Heel Raise
Hip Extension
Toe Raise

Bench Press
Barbell Row
High Pull
Triceps Extension
Superman
Abdominal Crunch

Microcycle 2
Weeks 5-8

2x week, Monday, Thursday (4 x 6) 2x week, Tuesday, Friday (4 x 6)

Squat
Leg Curl
Step up
Standing Heel Raise
Hip Extension
Toe Raise

Bench Press
Barbell Row
High Pull
Triceps Extension
Superman
Abdominal Crunch

Microcycle 3
Weeks 9-12

2x week, Monday, Thursday (5 x 4) 2x week, Tuesday, Friday (5 x 4)

Squat
Leg Curl
Step Up
Standing Heel Raise
Hip Extension
Toe Raise

Bench Press
Barbell Row
High Pull
Triceps Extension
Superman
Abdominal Crunch

Unloading Week
Week 13

2x week, Tuesday Thursday, 3 sets 6 reps each exercise

Lunge
Standing Heel Raise
High Pull

Endurance Mesocycle-Endurance Athlete

Microcycle 1
Weeks 1-4

Given the importance of maintaining power outputs (muscle endurance) in endurance sports, this mesocycle is an important component of these athletes resistance training protocol.

3x week, Monday, Wednesday, Friday, 4 sets 15 reps each exercise

Squat
Hamstring Curl
Hip Flexion
Heel Raise
Machine Bench Press
Crunch

Microcycle 2
Weeks 5-8

3x week, Monday, Wednesday, Friday, 4 sets 15 reps each exercise

Squat
Step Up
Heel Raise
Dumbbell Bench Press
Crunch
Dead Lift
Hip extension
Hamstring Curl
Shrug

Microcycle 3
Weeks 9-12

3x week, Monday, Wednesday, Friday, 4 sets 18 reps each exercise

Squat
Step Up
Heel Raise
Dumbbell Bench Press
Crunch
Superman
Hip extension
Hamstring Curl
High Pull

Unloading Week
Week 13

2x week, Tuesday Thursday, 3 sets 6 reps each exercise

Lunge
Standing Heel Raise
Step Ups

Weekend Warrior

Ok, so many of you may not fit the athlete profile, but it is likely that you have engaged in a few "pick-up" games of basketball or baseball. And if so, you may have "tweaked a knee" or ankle or you have just gotten worn out from the hard work. In any case, a general resistance training program will help you improve strength and speed, reduce injury, and improve overall balance and coordination. In other words, if you add a little training to your regular weekly activities, you'll not only feel better, you'll play better too.

The prototypical Weekend Warrior is classified as the "white collar" worker by day and semi-athlete on weekends. This means that you have a high stress office-type lifestyle, probably do not eat properly, but expect to be able to put out a good effort at 9am Saturday morning with your buddies on the court. If you think resistance training is for athletes or rehab, you need to think again. Resistance training should be thought of as injury prevention and performance enhancement. You should consider lifting 1 to 3 times weekly for about 1 hour per day. In other words, it is time to follow some of the programs we have outlined and perhaps move to Athlete status.

The major difference for these weekend warriors is that volume is generally less than that used by athletes. If you classify yourself as a weekend warrior type, but can handle higher levels of activity and still recover for work, then you might want to modify the workout below by adding some of the components of the athlete's workout. Just remember that these changes should be made gradually to allow your body to adapt to the training stresses.

Hypertrophy Mesocycle-Weekend Warrior
Microcycle 1
Weeks 1-4

This phase is designed to improve overall technique and muscular size. Twice a week is sufficient to stimulate growth; however, if you have a third day available, you can certainly give it a go.

2x week, Monday, Thursday, 3 sets 12 reps each exercise

Leg Press
Seated Hamstring Curl
Lat Pulldown
Triceps Pushdown
Leg Extension
Machine Bench Press
Bicep Curl
Abdominal Crunches

Microcycle 2
Weeks 5-8

2x week, Monday, Thursday, 3 sets 12 reps each exercise

Step Ups
Lying Hamstring Curl
Cable Row
Abdominal Crunches
Dumbbell Lunge
Dumbbell Bench Press
Machine Shoulder Press

Microcycle 3
Weeks 9-12

2x week, Monday, Thursday 3 sets 10 reps each exercise

Squat
Incline Dumbbell Bench Press
Machine Row
Abdominal Crunches
Leg Extension
Seated Leg Curl
Upright Row

Unloading Week
Week 13

2x week, Tuesday Thursday, 3 sets 6 reps each exercise

Squat
Machine Bench Press
Lat Pulldown

Strength Mesocycle-Weekend Warrior

Microcycle 1
Weeks 1-4

In your busy lifestyle, there is little time to hit 3 big workouts per week. Splits similar to athletes are acceptable. Since strength and power cycles use relatively high intensities we advised that included in these cycles be sufficient recovery time.

3x week, Monday, Wednesday, Friday (3 x 8)

Machine Bench Press
Incline Dumbbell Bench Press
Leg Press
Leg Extension
Abdominal Crunch
Cable Row
Lat Pulldown
Dumbbell Lunge
Lying Leg Curl

Microcycle 2
Weeks 5-8

3x week, Monday, Wednesday, Friday (3 x 8)

Incline Machine Bench Press
Seated Shoulder Press
Dead Lift
Glute Ham Raise
Assisted Chin Ups
Upright Row
Step Up
Pelvis Thrust

Microcycle 3
Weeks 9-12

3x week, Monday, Wednesday, Friday (4 x 6)

Dumbbell Bench Press
Assisted Pull Ups
Squat
Lying Leg Curl
Assisted Dips
Barbell Row
Lunge
Twisting Crunch

Unloading Week
Week 13

2x week, Tuesday Thursday, 3 sets 6 reps each exercise

Dead Lift
Dumbbell Bench Press
Machine Row

Power Mesocycle-Weekend Warrior
Microcycle 1
Weeks 1-4

Generally, power training for weekend warriors is dropped to twice per week and exercises are combined. Since this group has demands (such as work, classes, and other personal commitments) that many athletes do not face, overtraining and injury are cause for concern because recovery usually takes longer. For most people, a 4-6 week cycle will be plenty.

3x week, Monday, Wednesday, Friday (4 x 6)

Squat
Bench Press
Military Press
Lunge
Barbell Row
Abdominal Crunch

Microcycle 2
Weeks 5-8

2-3x week, Monday, Wednesday, Friday (4 x 6)

Dead Lift
Incline Dumbbell Press
Twisting Abdominal Crunch
Step Up
Upright Row

Microcycle 3
Weeks 9-12

2x week, Monday, Wednesday, Friday (5 x 4)

Squat
Glute Ham Raise
Dumbbell Row
Lunge
Dumbbell Bench Press
Pelvic Thrust

Unloading Week
Week 13

2x week, Tuesday Thursday, 3 sets 6 reps each exercise

Incline Bench Press
Dumbbell Row
Lunge

Endurance Mesocycle-Non-Contact Sport

Microcycle 1
Weeks 1-4

Most likely, this is the cycle where you will spend most of your training time. This is a good basic strength and conditioning program emphasizing all the components of fitness necessary to help you stay in shape for those weekend matches. Work hard and fast keep rest short and add some cardiovascular training to keep the heart working.

2x week, Monday, Thursday, 4 sets 15 reps each exercise

Leg Press
Seated Hamstring Curl
Lat Pulldown
Leg Extension
Machine Bench Press
Twisting Crunch

Microcycle 2
Weeks 5-8

2x week, Monday, Thursday, 4 sets 15 reps each exercise

Dead Lift
Lying Hamstring Curl
Incline Dumbbell Bench Press
Step Up
Assisted Chin Ups
Pelvic Thrust

Microcycle 3
Weeks 9-12

2x week, Monday, Thursday, 4 sets 18 reps each exercise

Squat
Bench Press
Abdominal Crunches
Lunge
Barbell Row

Unloading Week
Week 13

2x week, Tuesday Thursday, 3 sets 6 reps each exercise

Incline Dumbbell Press
Assisted Chin Ups
Step Ups

Non-Athlete Training

One of the most important applications of resistance training that has reemerged in recent years is the promotion of general health and fitness. These programs have habitually ignored the concept of periodization to the detriment of the lifters who have used them. The three workouts given below use a simple periodization pattern to provide recovery periods for the health and fitness enthusiast.

Health and Fitness

This workout is designed to compliment cardiovascular and flexibility training programs that should accompany its use. Unlike the athletic programs presented above, you will note a rapid decline in volume of training during the second mesocycle. This decline is designed to allow increases in cardiovascular training. In this way the training of different energy systems can be addressed. Also we concentrate heavily during the early mesocycles on machine lifts and later move to free weights. However, you should feel free to move freely between machine and free weight lifts once you have established a strength base.

Hypertrophy Mesocycle-Health and Fitness
Microcycle 1
Weeks 1-4

This phase is designed to improve overall technique and increase the size and strength of muscle and connective tissue. We recommend three days a week since this training is not being done in conjunction with competitive athletic training.

2x week, Monday, Thursday, 1 set moving to 3 sets of 12 reps each exercise

Leg Press or Leg Extension
Machine Bench Press
Military press
Bicep Curl
Standing Heel Raise
Abdominal Crunches

Hamstring Curl
Seated Row
Lat Pulldown
Triceps Pushdown
Toe Raises

Microcycle 2
Weeks 5-8

3 moving to 2x week, 3 sets 12 reps each exercise

Hamstring Curl or Deadlift
Machine or Free Weight Bench Press
Triceps Pushdown or Skull Crusher
Toe Raises

Leg Press or Squat
Seated or Bent Over Row
Lat Pulldown
Abdominal Crunches

Military press using Dumbbells, Bar or Machine
Bicep Curl using Dumbbells, Bar or Machine
Standing alternating with Sitting Heel Raise

Microcycle 3
Weeks 9-12

2x week, Monday, Thursday 3 moving to 1 sets 10 reps each exercise

Leg Press or Squat or Leg Extension
Machine or Free Weight Bench Press
Triceps Pushdown or Skull Crusher
Toe Raises
Hamstring Curl or Deadlift
Seated or Bent Over Row
Lat Pulldown
Abdominal Crunches
Bicep Curl using Dumbbells, Bar or Machine
Standing alternating with Sitting Heel Raise
Military press using Dumbbells, Bar or Machine

Unloading Week
Week 13

No lifting necessary

<u>Strength Mesocycle-Health and Fitness</u>
Microcycle 1
Weeks 1-4

Just as was the case during the hypertrophy cycle, the strength cycle will incorporate a significant taper after the middle of the overall mesocycle period. If you wish to add additional exercises you may incorporate a split routine as shown in the competitive athletes' workouts.

3x week, Monday, Wednesday, Friday (3 x 8)

Machine Bench Press
Military Press
Lat Pulldown
Triceps Extension
Abdominal Crunch
Leg Extension
Lying Leg Curl
Arm Curl
Cable Row
Leg Press

Microcycle 2
Weeks 5-8

3 to 2x week, Monday, Wednesday, Friday (3 x 8)

Leg Press or Squat or Leg Extension
Machine or Free Weight Bench Press
Lat Pulldown
Triceps Pushdown or Skull Crusher
Bicep Curl using Dumbbells, Bar or Machine
Standing alternating with Sitting Heel Raise
Military press using Dumbbells, Bar or Machine
Hamstring Curl or Deadlift
Seated or Bent Over Row
Toe Raises
Abdominal Crunches

Microcycle 3
Weeks 9-12

2 going to 1x week, 4 going to 2 sets of 6 reps

Leg Press or Squat or Leg Extension
Hamstring Curl or Deadlift
Machine or Free Weight Bench Press
Seated or Bent Over Row
Military press using Dumbbells, Bar or Machine
Lat Pulldown
Bicep Curl using Dumbbells, Bar or Machine
Triceps Pushdown or Skull Crusher
Standing alternating with Sitting Heel Raise
Toe Raises
Abdominal Crunches

Unloading Week
Week 13

Recovery without lifting

__Power Mesocycle-Health and Fitness__
Microcycle 1
Weeks 1-4

Although power training was once considered the sole property of the competitive athlete, we now recognize its importance in daily life. We present here a 13-week cycle although most people find a 4-6 week cycle sufficient. For this cycle we recommend reducing the resistance to weights that could be performed 12-15 times. We also suggest the use of rubber tubing or bands, as well as aquatic exercise for power training.

3x week, Monday, Wednesday, Friday (4 x 6)

Leg Press or Squat or Leg Extension
Hamstring Curl or Deadlift
Machine or Free Weight Bench Press
Seated or Bent Over Row
Military press using Dumbbells, Bar or Machine
Lat Pulldown
Bicep Curl using Dumbbells, Bar or Machine
Triceps Pushdown or Skull Crusher
Standing alternating with Sitting Heel Raise
Toe Raises
Abdominal Crunches

Microcycle 2
Weeks 5-8

3 going to 2 x week, 4sets of 6reps

Leg Press or Squat or Leg Extension
Hamstring Curl or Deadlift
Machine or Free Weight Bench Press
Seated or Bent Over Row
Military press using Dumbbells, Bar or Machine
Lat Pulldown
Bicep Curl using Dumbbells, Bar or Machine
Triceps Pushdown or Skull Crusher
Standing alternating with Sitting Heel Raise
Toe Raises
Abdominal Crunches

Microcycle 3
Weeks 9-12

2 moving to 1 x week, 2-1set x 6 reps

Leg Press or Squat or Leg Extension
Hamstring Curl or Deadlift
Machine or Free Weight Bench Press
Seated or Bent Over Row
Military press using Dumbbells, Bar or Machine
Lat Pulldown
Bicep Curl using Dumbbells, Bar or Machine
Triceps Pushdown or Skull Crusher
Standing alternating with Sitting Heel Raise
Toe Raises
Abdominal Crunches

Unloading Week
Week 13

Recovery without lifting

Endurance Mesocycle-Health and Fitness

Microcycle 1
Weeks 1-4

This training cycle can use either machine or free weight lifts. It is designed to increase your muscles' capacity to deal with increasing waste products during repeated contractions. This is an important factor in improving the efficiency of you daily activities.

2x week, 3 sets 15-20 reps each exercise

Leg Press or Squat or Leg Extension
Hamstring Curl or Deadlift
Machine or Free Weight Bench Press
Seated or Bent Over Row
Military press using Dumbbells, Bar or Machine
Lat Pulldown
Bicep Curl using Dumbbells, Bar or Machine
Triceps Pushdown or Skull Crusher
Standing alternating with Sitting Heel Raise
Toe Raises
Abdominal Crunches

Microcycle 2
Weeks 5-8

2x week, 3-2 sets 15 reps each exercise

Leg Press or Squat or Leg Extension
Hamstring Curl or Deadlift
Machine or Free Weight Bench Press
Seated or Bent Over Row
Military press using Dumbbells, Bar or Machine
Lat Pulldown
Bicep Curl using Dumbbells, Bar or Machine
Triceps Pushdown or Skull Crusher
Standing alternating with Sitting Heel Raise
Toe Raises
Abdominal Crunches

Microcycle 3
Weeks 9-12

2x week, 2-1 sets 15 reps each exercise

Leg Press or Squat or Leg Extension
Hamstring Curl or Deadlift
Machine or Free Weight Bench Press
Seated or Bent Over Row
Military press using Dumbbells, Bar or Machine
Lat Pulldown
Bicep Curl using Dumbbells, Bar or Machine
Triceps Pushdown or Skull Crusher
Standing alternating with Sitting Heel Raise
Toe Raises
Abdominal Crunches

Unloading Week
Week 13

Full recovery, no lifting

Body Composition

In describing this workout we have avoided the term weight loss, since changes in body composition are a combination of losing body fat and increasing lean body mass (muscle, bone and connective tissue). As we noted earlier, resistance training is effective in addressing body composition changes because it is a high-intensity interval workout. Since these workouts are designed for targeting body composition and not competitive performance, we have concentrated on machine lifts rather than free weights. However, free weights can be utilized if you desire.

Hypertrophy Mesocycle-Body Composition
Microcycle 1
Weeks 1-4

This phase is designed to improve overall technique and increase the size and strength of muscle and connective tissue. We recommend three days a week since this training is not being done in conjunction with competitive athletic training.

2x week, Monday, Thursday, 1 set moving to 3 sets of 12 reps each exercise

Leg Press or Leg Extension
Machine Bench Press
Military press
Bicep Curl
Standing Heel Raise
Abdominal Crunches
Hamstring Curl
Seated Row
Lat Pulldown
Triceps Pushdown
Toe Raises

Microcycle 2
Weeks 5-8

3 moving to 2 x week, 3 sets 12 reps each exercise

Leg Press or Leg Extension
Machine Bench Press
Military press
Bicep Curl
Standing Heel Raise
Abdominal Crunches
Hamstring Curl
Seated Row
Lat Pulldown
Triceps Pushdown
Toe Raises

Microcycle 3
Weeks 9-12

2x week, Monday, Thursday 3 moving to 1 sets 10 reps each exercise

Leg Press or Leg Extension
Machine Bench Press
Military press
Bicep Curl
Standing Heel Raise
Abdominal Crunches
Hamstring Curl
Seated Row
Lat Pulldown
Triceps Pushdown
Toe Raises

Unloading Week
Week 13

No lifting necessary

Strength Mesocycle-Body Composition

Microcycle 1
Weeks 1-4

Here we shorten both the strength and power cycles in favor of the hypertrophy and endurance cycles.

3x week, Monday, Wednesday, Friday (3 sets x 8-12 reps)

Leg Press or Leg Extension
Hamstring Curl
Machine Bench Press
Seated Row
Military press
Lat Pulldown
Bicep Curl
Triceps Pushdown
Standing Heel Raise
Toe Raises
Abdominal Crunches

Microcycle 2
Weeks 5-8

3 to 1 x week, Monday, Wednesday, Friday (3 sets x 8 reps)

Leg Press or Leg Extension
Hamstring Curl
Machine Bench Press
Seated Row
Military press
Lat Pulldown
Bicep Curl
Triceps Pushdown
Standing Heel Raise
Toe Raises
Abdominal Crunches

Unloading Weeks
Week 9 and10

Recovery without lifting

Power Mesocycle-Health and Fitness

Microcycle 1
Weeks 1-4

The power cycle not only increases power it also provides a high intensity overload by increasing speed of movement while reducing load. This allows a high caloric output while addressing movement speed. We have also increased the number of repetitions to 10-12, and we suggest reducing the weight to 60-65 percent of that dictated by these repetition figures. We have reduced the length of this cycle in favor of the hypertrophy and endurance cycles.

3x week, Monday, Wednesday, Friday (3 sets x 10-12 reps)

Leg Press or Leg Extension
Machine Bench Press
Standing Heel Raises
Abdominal Crunches
Lat Pulldown
Triceps Pushdown
Hamstring Curl
Toe Raises
Seated Row
Military press
Bicep Curl

Microcycle 2
Weeks 5-8

3 going to 1 x week, 3 sets of 8-10 reps

Leg Press or Leg Extension
Machine Bench Press
Military press
Bicep Curl
Standing Heel Raise
Abdominal Crunches
Hamstring Curl
Seated Row
Lat Pulldown
Triceps Pushdown
Toe Raises

Unloading Week
Weeks 9 and 10

Recovery without lifting

Endurance Mesocycle-Body Composition
Microcycle 1
Weeks 1-4

For this cycle we are encouraging the use of a circuit training pattern. This pattern of lifting will reduce recovery time between sets while increasing the number of repetitions. In addition, muscles will recover during the training since repeated sets for a specific muscle will occur only after the entire circuit is completed.

3x week, 3 sets 18-20 reps each exercise

Leg Press or Leg Extension
Machine Bench Press
Military press
Bicep Curl
Standing Heel Raise
Abdominal Crunches
Hamstring Curl
Seated Row
Lat Pulldown
Triceps Pushdown
Toe Raises

Microcycle 2
Weeks 5-8

3x week, 3-2 sets 18-20 reps each exercise

Leg Press or Leg Extension
Machine Bench Press
Military press
Bicep Curl
Standing Heel Raise
Abdominal Crunches
Hamstring Curl
Seated Row
Lat Pulldown
Triceps Pushdown
Toe Raises

Microcycle 3
Weeks 9-12

3x week, 2-1 sets 18-20 reps each exercise

Leg Press or Leg Extension
Machine Bench Press
Military press
Bicep Curl
Standing Heel Raise
Abdominal Crunches
Hamstring Curl
Seated Row
Lat Pulldown
Triceps Pushdown
Toe Raises

Unloading Week
Week 13

Full recovery, no lifting

Older Lifters

For older lifters we recommend a prolonged hypertrophy period to allow tissues to adapt to the stresses of lifting. After that all other cycles have been reduced to four weeks since our data indicate that this is the optimal duration for these training cycles by older adults. Additionally, we typically use translational cycles with older individuals. These are drills that simulate activities of daily living in recreational-type training.

Hypertrophy Mesocycle-Body Composition

Microcycle 1

Weeks 1-4

This constitutes a tissue adaptation period to assure that the muscle and connective tissues of our older lifters can be ready for the increased stresses associated with resistance training. Additionally we recommend that the resistance used starts at a minimal weight and increases progressively to the 8-12 repetition figure weight over the entire mesocycle.

2x week, 1 set moving to 2 sets of 8-12 reps each exercise

Leg Press or Leg Extension
Machine Bench Press
Military press
Bicep Curl
Standing Heel Raise
Abdominal Crunches
Hamstring Curl
Seated Row
Lat Pulldown
Triceps Pushdown
Toe Raises

Microcycle 2

Weeks 5-8

2 moving to 3 x week, 2 moving to 3 sets 8-12 reps each exercise

Leg Press or Leg Extension
Machine Bench Press
Military press
Bicep Curl
Standing Heel Raise
Abdominal Crunches
Hamstring Curl
Seated Row
Lat Pulldown
Triceps Pushdown
Toe Raises

Microcycle 3

Weeks 9-12

3 moving to 2 x week, 3 moving to 1 sets 8-12 reps each exercise

Leg Press or Leg Extension
Machine Bench Press
Military press
Bicep Curl
Standing Heel Raise
Abdominal Crunches
Hamstring Curl
Seated Row
Lat Pulldown
Triceps Pushdown
Toe Raises

Unloading Week
Week 13

No lifting necessary

<u>*Strength Mesocycle-Older Persons*</u>

Microcycle 1
Weeks 1-4

Here we shorten both the strength cycles since our data indicate a plateau in response to the training by week 4.

3 x week, Monday, Wednesday, Friday (2 sets x 8-12 reps)

Leg Press or Leg Extension
Machine Bench Press
Military press
Bicep Curl
Standing Heel Raise
Leg Abduction
Abdominal Crunches
Hamstring Curl
Seated Row
Lat Pulldown
Triceps Pushdown
Toe Raises
Leg Adduction

Unloading Weeks
Week 5 and 6

Recovery without lifting. Translational training.

<u>*Power Mesocycle-Health and Fitness*</u>

Microcycle 1
Weeks 1-4

The power cycle may be one of the most important cycles for improving functional performance in older persons. Here we use resistances of 60% of the 10-12 rep figure that would normally be dictated by the number of reps indicated. Additionally we recommend the use of hydraulic, pneumatic, rubber band and tubes, and or aquatic resistance to reduce the probability of injury from inertia associated with machine and free weights.

3 x week, Monday, Wednesday, Friday (3-2 sets x 10-12 reps)

Leg Press or Leg Extension
Machine Bench Press
Military press
Bicep Curl
Standing Heel Raise
Abdominal Crunches
Hamstring Curl
Seated Row
Lat Pulldown
Triceps Pushdown
Toe Raises

Unloading Week
Weeks 5 and 6

Recovery without lifting. Translational training

Endurance Mesocycle-Older Persons
Microcycle 1
Weeks 1-4

The endurance cycle is important to older individuals since the ability to repeat movements of daily living is imperative for maintenance of independence and fall prevention.

3 x week, 1 going to 2 and back to 1 set, 15-18 reps per exercise

Leg Press or Leg Extension
Machine Bench Press
Military press
Bicep Curl
Standing Heel Raise
Abdominal Crunches

Hamstring Curl
Seated Row
Lat Pulldown
Triceps Pushdown
Toe Raises

Unloading Week
Weeks 5 and 6

Full recovery, no lifting. Translational training.

Conclusion

Recognize that the workouts provided in this chapter are examples of workouts that can be used with specific population. These workout can be modified, mixed, and matched using the information and knowledge you have developed in reading this book so that you can target your own goals and maximize your results.

Chapter

11

The Myths of Weight-Training

If you spend or have spent any time around the gym, health club or wellness center, you know it is a treasury of information... some good, some bad. Therefore, the things you hear range in truth from true to the best of our knowledge at this point (always a good idea to hedge your bets a bit) to complete fiction. Let's look at a few of the "old standards" and "new dogmas" and react to each. We have attempted to classify the statements using individual topic headings.

Body Tissues

If you lift weights you'll get muscle bound and won't even be able to scratch your back.

This statement has not only been disproved, but actually the opposite is true. When weight-training exercises are performed through a full range of motion, they will actually increase your range of motion and flexibility. If you will recall the section on muscle growth in Chapter 2, we noted that muscles not only add cross-sectional are (size) when weight trained, they can also add length by adding more contractile units (sarcomeres). The only argument that can be made to support this statement is that when two

Figure 11-1

muscle groups push against each other, like the forearm and biceps, they can go no further. However, rather than a physiological reduction in range of motion, this might more accurately in terms of physics by the expression "two objects cannot occupy the same space at the same time".

You can turn your fat to muscle, but when you stop lifting it will turn back into fat.

Let's make this very simple Figure 11-2 presents microscopic pictures of muscle and fat. Muscle is one kind of tissue, fat is another, and one cannot become the other. End of story! The reasons why muscle may appear to be "turning into fat" are summarized below:

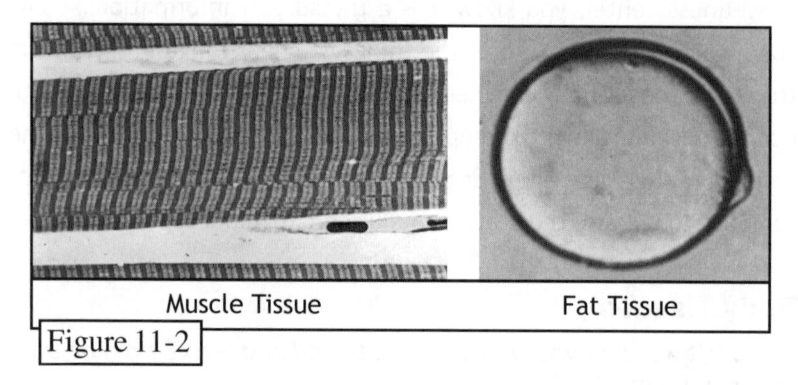

Figure 11-2

- Reduced training causes a reduction in muscle size,
- The number of calories you burn when training blows away the number of calories you burn when not training,
- You will most likely take in the same number of calories or more when you're not training as when you are,
- This extra energy will be stored as fat.

So, smaller muscles and bigger fat cells make it appear that you have changed your muscle to fat.

You can't change muscle fiber types, they're dictated by genetics.

Not only is this not true, most muscle physiologists would agree that muscles are highly plastic and will show considerable change with training. In fact, we even know the nature of the change that will occur, from type 2D to type 2A muscle. If you look back at the section on muscle types in Chapter 2, you will see that the latest muscle fiber typing scheme presents both "pure" and "hybrid" muscle types, with the hybrids being a mixture of proteins from the neighboring pure muscle fiber types.

PAIN AND GAIN

The soreness you feel a couple of days after lifting is lactic acid burning your muscles.

This is simply not true. Although lactate levels will rise during lifting, they will most likely return to near baseline levels within minutes of completing an exercise. The pain you feel a few days after exercise is the result of inflammation caused by microscopic muscle damage, a kind of microscopic intra-muscle equivalent of hitting yourself in the thumb with a hammer. For a more detailed description we refer you to the section on delayed onset of muscle soreness (DOMS) in Chapter 2.

You must work to failure to increase a muscle's size and/or strength.

This is one of those "not absolutely true and not absolutely false" statements. There is no doubt that high levels of overload are necessary to increase strength and hypertrophy muscles. However, there is little evidence indicating that "going to failure" is a requirement for maximizing either. Intensity and volume are more important than failure when attempting to increase strength and hypertrophy, respectively. In addition, going to failure every session will most likely lead to overtraining and a reduction in training capacity, thereby reducing rather than increasing strength and hypertrophy (see Chapter 9: Periodization).

Figure 11-3

The more your muscles burn during a lift, the bigger and stronger they will get.

This is one of those "no pain, no gain" or beyond to "more pain, more gain" adages. There are certainly conflicting data as to the importance of waste product build-ups as stimuli for increasing muscle size. Most data, however, do not support a linear relationship between "burn" and muscular strength or size increases.

LIFTING SAFETY

Never hold your breath when weight-training.

Not holding your breath during a lift is, for most lifts, very sound advice. Holding your breath during a heavy muscular exertion, called performing a "Valsalva maneuver", can lead to large changes in blood pressure and the potential for cardiovascular accident or rupture of smaller blood vessels (see Figure 11-4). But just as was the case with our other "myths" there are exceptions to the statement. It is clear that when performing heavy multi-joint lifts involving risk to the lower back, such as the squat, that holding your breath through the most critical part of the lift may increase intra-abdominal pressure and reduce the risk of lower back injury. In fact, the reason a weight-lifting belt is effective in providing support for the lower back is not because it provides physical support to the back. Rather, the lifter exerts force against the belt using his or her abdominal muscles and thereby increases intra-abdominal pressure offers support and protects the lower back.

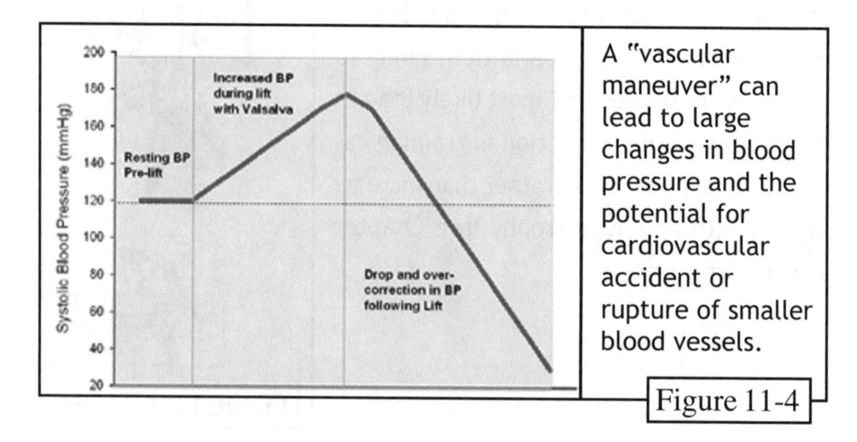

A "vascular maneuver" can lead to large changes in blood pressure and the potential for cardiovascular accident or rupture of smaller blood vessels.

Figure 11-4

CONTORTIONS AND DISTORTIONS

The best way to work your lats during a lat pulldown is to pull the bar behind your neck.

This method of lifting is so prominent in the gym that we examined the muscle activity during the lat pulldown performed in front of the clavicle and behind the neck and under two other conditions. Our findings were clear, significantly greater electrical activity was generated by the lats when the lat pulldown was performed pulling the bar down in front of the head, to the clavicle, than was generated by pulling it down behind the neck or in any other position. (see Figure 11-5)

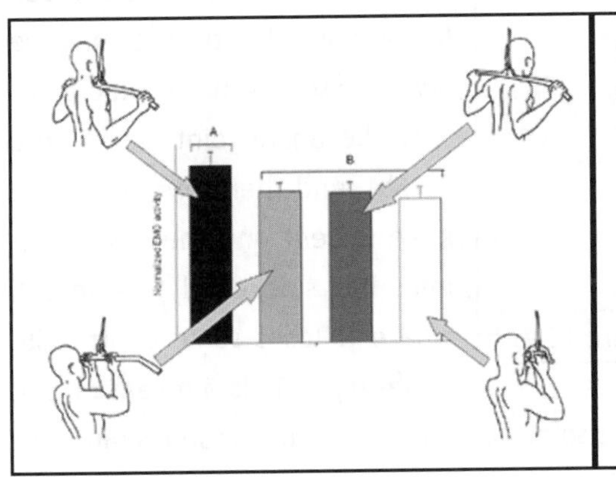

Significantly greater electrical activity is generated by the lats when the lat pulldown is performed pulling the bar down in front of the head, to the clavicle.

Figure 11-5

You can target different muscles of your quads during the squat and leg extension by changing the position of your feet.

The truth of this statement is dependent on the exercise you're considering. Both our laboratory and others have shown that changes in foot position (toes in, toes neutral, and toes out) have little or no affect on targeting specific muscles of the quads during the squat. So don't try to bend your body into some convoluted shape in a futile attempt to target one muscle fiber sitting on the outermost region of your vastus lateralis. You just can't do it during a squat. The best bet is to find a safe and comfortable foot position and go from there.

For the leg extension, however, it appears to be quite a different story. From the studies we have seen some fairly safe assumptions can be made. All results indicate that the vastus lateralis can most effectively be targeted using a "toes in" position. The results for the rectus femoris and vastus medialis are not as clear, but most of the data seem to favor a "toes out" position to target these two muscles.

The seated heal raise is the best way to work your calves.

In actuality you can target different muscles in your calves by performing seated or straight-leg heel raises. The lateral and medial portions of the gastrocnemeius muscle cross both the knee and ankle joints (see Figure 11-6a). Therefore the amount of tension on this muscle and it's level of use can be increased by straightening the leg. The soleus, however, crosses only the ankle joint (see Figure 11-6b), and therefore, when the knee is bent and the gastrocnemius has slackened to a length where it loses some contractile capacity. This increases the amount of activity in the soleus as it takes greater responsibility for the movement. Bottom line, target the soleus with bent knee (seated) heel raises and the gastrocnemius with straight leg (standing or straight leg in the leg press machine) heel raises.

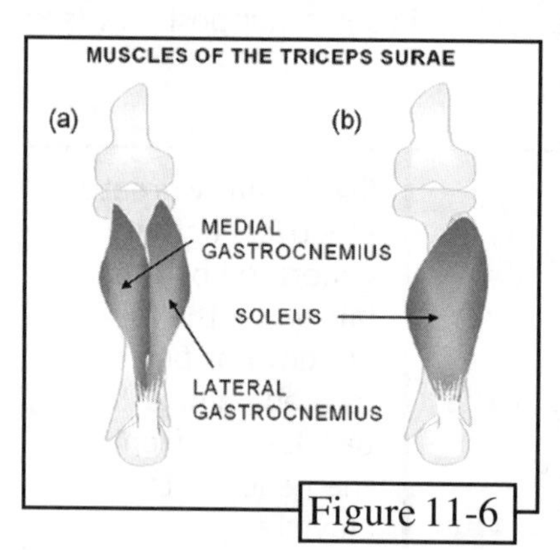

Figure 11-6

You can target different areas of your pecs by using different handgrip distances and bench inclines.

This one is true although the results may go against what your intuition tells you, at least when it comes to grip width. The two areas of the chest with which we are most concerned are the middle portion adjacent to the sternum (sternocostal area) and the outside upper portion closer to the clavicle (clavicular fibers). The wide grip is most effective in targeting the sternocostal fibers, while the narrow grip targets the clavicular fibers. Targeting lower, middle, and upper areas of the pecs is possible using the declined, flat and inclined positions, respectively, during the lift. If you will recall we discussed this in chapter 3 in describing lifting vectors (see Figures 3-8a and 3-8b). One interesting fact is that the flat bench press has been shown to be nearly as effective as the inclined bench in targeting the upper fibers and the declined bench in targeting the lower fibers, so if your time is limited the good old flat bench press is your best bet.

The Smith machine is the safest place to do a squat and is better at targeting the glutes.

Figure 11-7 shows the squat exercise performed using free weights and in the Smith machine. Although we may believe we are moving the bar in a straight line during the squat, the trajectory of the bar actually forms a slight forward arc caused by the sequential addition of the arcs produced about the ankle, knee; hip, and lower back. This arc is not possible in the Smith machine since it dictates that the bar move in a straight line. To compensate for this, most people are

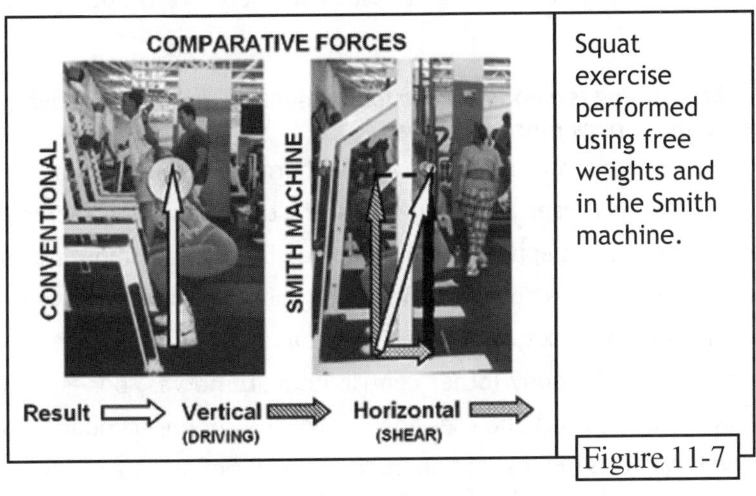

Squat exercise performed using free weights and in the Smith machine.

Figure 11-7

forced to place their feet a good distance in front of the bar if they wish to reach anywhere near a 90 degree knee angle. As Figure 11-7 shows this means that part of the force that would normally drive the bar vertically in the free weight squat is directed horizontally in the Smith squat creating shearing forces at the knee hip and lower back. In addition, in EMG analyses of the two lifts we were able to detect no advantage of one lift over the other in targeting the gluts.

WEIGHT-TRAINING AND WEIGHT CONTROL

The slower you lift the more fat you'll burn during a workout.

This statement is probably a carry-over from the old "work slow to burn fat" adage. While there is no problem with slow controlled movements, and from a safety standpoint they are highly desirable, especially for the beginning lifter, the assumption that the slower you lift the more fat you'll burn has a number of things working against it. The first problem is that intensity of exercise appears to have the greatest impact on calories burned both during and after exercise. In fact, intensity has been shown to be a more important determinant of overall daily energy expenditure than exercise duration. The second problem is that prolonged slow-speed lifting produces a high level of waste product build-up in the muscle that may reduce the overall intensity and volume of the work cycle during the lifting program. In short, intensity rather than duration seems to be a more important controlling factor for burning calories and therefore reducing body fat.

Weight-training is a good way to lose weight because the increased muscle mass uses more calories.

While there is no doubt that muscles burn more calories than fat, stating that increases in muscle mass are the controlling factor in weight loss doesn't appear to be supported by simple computations. Skeletal muscle uses about 2.5 times the energy of fat (13.14 versus 4.53kcal/kg/day), but it only makes up about 44% of the fat free mass (FFM) of the body (other contributors are nerves, bones, ligaments, tendons, etc.) and uses about 3% of the energy accounted for by the FFM. This means that an increase in FFM of 10% (from 25% BF to 15%BF) would only add an average energy expenditure of about 34 kcal/day,

130 lbs x 1kg/2.2lb x .85FFM X .44 of FFM X 13.14Kcal/kg/day = 290.39 Kcal
130 lbs x 1kg/2.2lb x .75FFM X .44 of FFM X 13.14Kcal/kg/day = <u>256.22 Kcal</u>
34.17 Kcal

hardly enough to account for the success of resistance training in reducing body fat.

SETS, REPS AND SPEED

Always lift using slow, controlled movements.

There is no doubt that the majority of the texts on resistance-training suggest the use of slow, controlled movements to increase strength and muscle mass, and to maximize safety. However, there are a large number of experts in the field that argue that high-velocity training is necessary to maximize power development. This opinion is countered by other fitness professionals who say that high-velocity training should not be used in the weight-room, because it is ballistic in nature and has a high injury potential. These individuals argue that the correct venue for speed training is outside the weight room, on the field, gym floor, or track. Given the existing information, both opinions are valid and should be respected. Possibly the opinion gap between these groups can be reduced by using the low-inertia resistance training methods we have presented in this text during high-speed training.

The slower you lift the bigger and stronger your muscles will get.

This statement combines "no pain, no gain" principle with the "more is better" principle, both of which are not principles at all! While it might be true that keeping the muscle under tension for a period of time, doing multiple sets, controlling the speed of the movement and finding the optimal balance between lifting loads and repetitions, can maximize size gains, the concept that slower is better simply doesn't fly. Once again we can look at this statement using a logical progression;

- Intensity is the most important factor in stimulating strength gains, and therefore the load you can move during training and the velocity at which you move it is the greatest stimulus for strength and power,
- The load you move multiplied by the number of sets and reps you do equals your lifting volume,
- Very slow lifting increases waste product build-up decreasing both the intensity at which you can perform a set and the number of reps and sets you can do,

- Since volume is the major stimulus for hypertrophy, very slow lifting will most likely also be less effective than standard lifting techniques in increasing muscle size.

One set is as good as multiple sets when lifting.

There are a number of studies that would seem to support this statement. In fact, reviews on the topic have noted that studies favoring the statement seem to outweigh those opposing it. However, some researchers have noted that those studies don't take into account all the factors that may affect the results of this comparison. These include the number of people in a study, the training level of the subjects, the muscle group or movement tested, and the nature of the lifting program employed. When these factors are considered, it appears that a more valid statement is that at the beginning of training, when people are at their lowest training levels, and therefore show the greatest response to training (see Figure 11-8), single set training appears to be as effective in increasing strength and muscle size as multiple set training. However, for the more advanced lifter, who has already begun to adapt to the training stimulus, multiple sets are more effective.

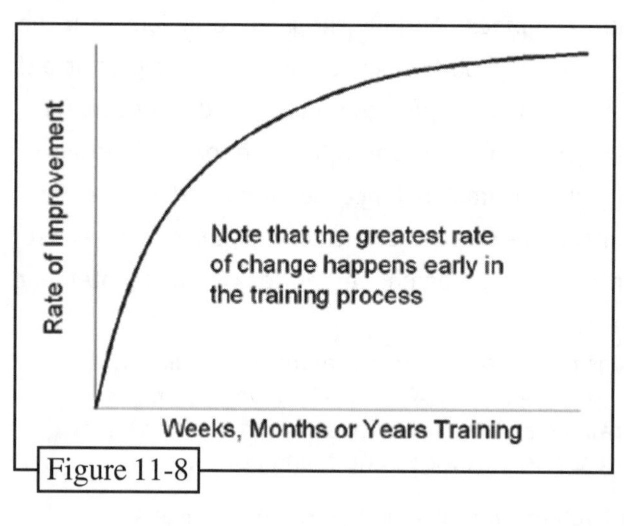

Figure 11-8

The best lifting method is to do 3 sets of 8-12 repetitions using 1-2 second concentric and 3-4 eccentric phases.

This lifting pattern was developed by bodybuilders to balance load, repetitions and fatigue to maximize the volume of work, and therefore hypertrophy. As you have seen in our chapter on training methods no single training pattern can address all the goals that can be accomplished during weight-training. If it could, this would be a very thin book and the topic of how to best design resistance-training programs would already be answered.

TRAINING CONSISTENCY

If you miss a day of training you'll lose all the gains you've made and have to start all over again.

This statement is not only false, it is harmful on a number of levels. First of all, it contradicts one of the most important training concepts that has come our way in the past few decades, periodization. As you will remember from Chapter 9, to maximize the gains resulting from weight-training you must use the proper patterns of work and recovery. Failure to do this can lead to overtraining and overuse injury. Secondly, it produces an "environment of failure" where missing a day of training is seen as a violation of the training rules and ruins all the work you have accomplished. This "guilt trip" is then used as an excuse not to lift the next day, the day after that, and the day after that, until months or even years go by without training. It is a much healthier attitude to see a few days of missed training as a recovery period during which your body will restructure itself to prepare for your next training session. Before we leave this section, however, let's make one thing clear, this concept should not be used as a rationalization to only train one or two days a week. Training consistency is important... it's training obsession that should be avoided.

Figure 11-9

Louie knew that if he stopped, he'd lose everything he'd worked for!

Never let the weights in a weight stack touch between repetitions since this allows the muscle to rest and you won't get maximal benefit from you lifting.

This one forgets some of the basic concepts that we have mentioned over and over again in this text. First of all, a period of recovery is a positive thing, even of it is only a momentary reduction in tension between reps. You should allow a momentary rest between reps so that oxygenated blood can effectively enter the muscle and waste products can be washed out. Remember, during a held contraction of over 60-70% of max the blood flow to your muscle is occluded. Therefore, momentary rests between reps can actually increase the intensity and volume of the work you are performing.

Figure 11-10

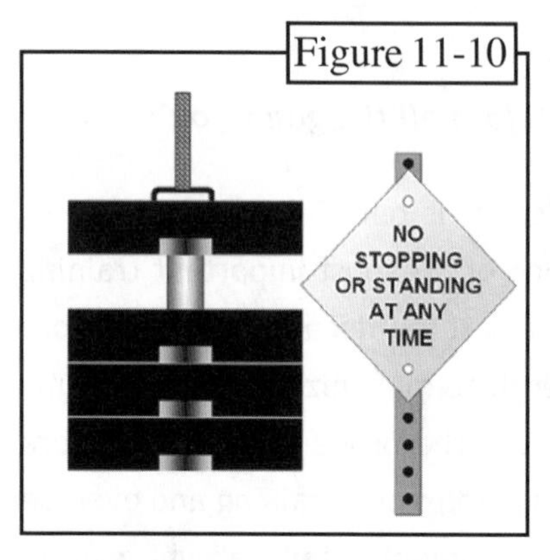

WELLNESS

If you employ Super Slow weight training you don't need to do cardiovascular exercise.

This is simply incorrect. While weight-training may have some positive effects on aerobic capacity, lipid profiles, and other health-related factors, it simply can not replace cardiovascular exercise. It is our contention that exercise programs designed to maximize health should employ both forms of exercise since they affect very different functional and systemic factors.

If you have a cold the best thing to do is go to the gym and sweat it out.

As we mentioned earlier in this text, the immediate response of the immune system to high-intensity training is actually to reduce its effectiveness and increase susceptibility to infection. So "sweating out a cold" in the gym would most likely be counterproductive and might even increase the level of illness.

Index